To see the invisible —
To dream the impossible —
To accomplish the incredible . . .

A DREAM COME TRUE

Publishing Consultant and Designer
Dave Turner and Associates
Paducah, Kentucky

Directed by:
Paul Parham
Director of Communications
ALSAC

Text by:
Hazel Fath
Memphis, Tennessee

Printed in Dallas, Texas by
Taylor Publishing Company

A DREAM COME TRUE

The Story of
St. Jude Children's Research Hospital
and
ALSAC

4

Introduction

This is the story of St. Jude Children's Research Hospital, the largest childhood cancer research center in the United States, located in Memphis, Tennessee.

Since the opening of the hospital twenty years ago, total medical care has been provided, at no direct cost to the patient, to more than seven thousand children who have been referred by their physicians and whose disease was under study at the hospital at the time of referral. These children have come from thirty-nine states in the United States and twenty-nine foreign countries.

The dedicated basic and clinical research staffs have shared and will continue to share their findings with physicians and scientists throughout the entire world as they constantly search for a cure that will end childhood cancer forever.

This is also the story of ALSAC, the organization dedicated to the support of the hospital, and its twenty-five years of providing funds to operate and maintain the hospital. It is the story of volunteers dedicated to seeing that the hospital's life-saving work will never be without the monies needed to carry it on.

Dedication

to DANNY THOMAS who dreamed the dream and inspired others to help make his dream a reality and whose continuing dedication serves as an inspiration to all . . .

to EDWARD F. BARRY who brought the dream to reality while devoting endless hours as President of the steering committee of the St. Jude Foundation of Memphis and as Chairman of the Board of Governors of St. Jude Children's Research Hospital . . .

to MICHAEL F. TAMER who organized the Arabic-speaking people of the United States in the formation of ALSAC for the sole purpose of raising funds for the continued maintenance of St. Jude Children's Research Hospital.

Table of Contents

One Man's Dream

Only once before had an entertainer made a vow to found a hospital for the poor and fulfilled that vow. And that was in the year 1123 A.D.!

The entertainer was Rahere, a man of humble birth and little education. In his youth he had frequented the houses of noblemen of England and had gained quite a reputation as a "jongleur". The jongleurs were a renowned class in medieval society. They earned their living as public entertainers — some by telling tales of early heroes, some by singing or playing a musical instrument, some by juggling and dancing — and were well respected throughout England and France.

Some of the jongleurs were permanent members of the households of the noblemen they entertained, but others, like Rahere, travelled from place to place and were well rewarded with gifts and money for their performances. Rahere became one of the most successful and respected of his profession and was well-known in the court of Henry I.

While he was on a pilgrimage to Rome, Rahere became very ill. Convinced that he was dying, he made a vow that if he were allowed to return to his beloved England he would found a hospital "for the restoration of poor men, and, as far as possible, would minister to the necessities of the poor gathered together in that place".

Rahere recovered from his illness and set out on the long voyage back to England. It is said that, on this trip, St. Bartholomew appeared to him in a vision. He was told to found his hospital, along with a church, in Smithfield, just outside the walls of the City of London. After receiving the blessing of both the King, to whom the land belonged, and the Bishop of London, Rahere began construction of his hospital and church. It was consecrated in 1129 A.D. and named for St. Bartholomew.

Under the protection of the King and the Bishop, Rahere helped run the hospital and continued to raise money for its operation. Throughout the Middle Ages gifts of money and property were made to it and from the revenues collected the hospital became fully endowed. It remained dedicated to the service of the poor who needed medical treatment.

It still stands, now called the Royal Hospital of Saint Bartholomew, still serving centuries later, the realization of one man's determination to fulfill a vow.

Amos Jacobs had never heard of Rahere the day in Detroit when he entered the Church of St. Peter and St. Paul seeking a solution to his many problems.

Like Rahere he was an entertainer — in local night clubs. He, too, wanted to make what he called the "big time". But the club where he was working was closing and it was a rough season for entertainers — for all Americans, in fact — in those last years of the Great Depression. But it did seem that young Amos had more than his share of problems.

His young wife was due to deliver their first child and he had no money for the hospital. In fact, all he had in his pocket was seven dollars and some change. His wife had suggested that he give up his dream of becoming an entertainer. She would gladly have settled for his working in any job that would pay the bills — store clerk, cab driver, factory worker, anything.

As Amos sat thinking about his problems in the quiet of the church, he picked up a pamphlet and began to read it. The leaflet was about the so-called "forgotten saint", Saint Jude Thaddeus, the patron saint of the impossible, hopeless and difficult cases. What case could be more hopeless than his?

He walked over to the prayer box, dropped in his seven dollars and asked St. Jude to return it to him tenfold. When Amos reached home there was a message asking him to do a radio commercial. The compensation would be seventy-five dollars, more than the tenfold for which he had prayed. Young Amos knew then that this saint was indeed a powerful influence in his life. He would choose St. Jude as his patron saint.

Shortly after his first encounter with St. Jude, and after the birth of his daughter, he received a call from the only person he knew in Chicago. This man had called Amos to offer him a job on the staff of the radio station where he worked. Again, Amos had the disturbing feeling that there was a definite guiding influence in his life. It had to be more than coincidence that this man would offer him a job that any number of out-of-work Chicago radio announcers could easily have filled.

Guided by this feeling, the young entertainer moved his wife and infant daughter to Chicago and went to work for the radio station. He also returned to the night club circuit in Chicago.

In August of 1940 he reported for a week's tryout at the 5100 Club on Chicago's north side. It wasn't the very best of clubs but he needed the money they would pay him. For this engagement he decided to change his name so that he would not blemish the name of Jacobs. He chose a combination of two of his brothers' names and called himself Danny Thomas.

Three years later he was still there — still Danny Thomas — and his salary had risen from fifty dollars a week to five hundred. The club was now one of the most popular in Chicago. And, once again, he was faced with another crisis. The manager-owner of the 5100 Club had offered him a partnership with terms that were very favorable to the young entertainer. The only provision was that he stay with the club as permanent master of ceremonies.

Once again he was faced with a career decision. He could take the security of being a saloonkeeper-entertainer and remain in that familiar environment. Or, he could continue toward his goal — to be a top comedian in the "big time".

As before, he turned to St. Jude. This time he prayed, "Help me find my place in life. Give me just a small sign of what road I must take and I'll dedicate my life to perpetuating your name."

"Help me find my place in life and I will build you a shrine . . . where the poor, and the helpless and the hopeless may come for comfort and aid."

"When I've been at the turning points — when I really needed help — St. Jude has been right there. Some people think I'm a nut for believing in miracles, but that's how I feel."

He left the church and made his way back to the club. He was to give the owner his answer by midnight. That night one of the biggest snowstorms of the season hit the Chicago area. All traffic, in and out of the city, was halted.

One of the many stranded that night in 1943 was Abe Lastfogel, a theatrical agent. A local representative suggested that they might kill some time by dropping into the 5100 Club to hear the comedian Danny Thomas. He thought Lastfogel might be interested in him.

Lastfogel was. He told Danny that his place was definitely in show business and that he could make him a star. This, to Danny, was St. Jude's answer to his prayer. He was to continue to try for the "Big time" and he was to do it as Danny Thomas.

Danny followed Abe Lastfogel to New York where Lastfogel was President of U.S.O. Camp Shows. Lastfogel sent Danny overseas with Marlene Dietrich to entertain the troops, the first engagement of thousands that he would book for the young man he had promised to make a star!

After the war, Danny once again found himself in Chicago. But in 1945 he was a star! He was headlining the show at the Chez Paree and he was making three thousand dollars a week!

One day, shortly after his return to Chicago, he was renewing old friendships and visiting old haunts. He decided to go back to St. Clement's church where he had prayed that day of the blizzard.

"I lit a candle before the marble statue of St. Clement. And then I looked closer at the statue. My hair stood on end! What I had assumed was a statue of St. Clement wasn't at all. It was St. Jude! I was dumbfounded. It was the most awe-inspiring moment in my life."

Danny continues the story, "I started thinking — about St. Jude. What he'd done for me. The

Danny Thomas

vow I'd made to him in return. The time had come to fulfill it."

He remembered a vow that his mother had made when he was small. He relates it to his vow. "I made a vow. I forgot it. Naturally when you get the wrinkles out of your stomach you forget you were hungry. You forget who fed you, too. That's human nature. A vow of emotion is the vow of a dying man — no one expects you to keep it."

"But my mother kept her vow. That stayed in the back of my mind," Danny said. "We Middle Easterners are prone to vow-making and fulfilling. So, how to keep mine? I could have gotten rid of the obligation quickly with a side altar. That's why I say that St. Jude Hospital, the institution, was predestined. The way I was brought up it would have been a grandiose fulfillment of the vow — a beautiful side altar in a church."

"There are several such shrines around the country. The original shrine of St. Jude is a side altar in the church of Our Lady of Guadalupe in the south side of Chicago. It's just a simple little altar in a simple little parish church founded in 1927 and it's protected and maintained by the Chicago police."

"On my knees in that church I had no idea of building a hospital. But I prospered and so did my dream."

From that day Danny Thomas moved toward the fulfillment of his vow. It would be many years before his dream would take the shape and form of St. Jude Children's Research Hospital.

"Help me find my place in life and I will build you a shrine . . . where the poor, and the helpless and the hopeless may come for comfort and aid."

With a Lot of Help from His Friends

Danny Thomas had a friend in a very high place — Samuel Cardinal Stritch of Chicago. The Cardinal had confirmed Danny when he was Bishop of Toledo. Danny had served as altar boy for him there. Whenever Danny was in Chicago, and his career took him there often, he would drop in to visit with the Cardinal.

One of the main subjects of conversation was Danny's dream to build a shrine to St. Jude. He thought he would like it to be a small hospital where children could be cared for regardless of race, creed or ability to pay ... a hospital where no suffering child would be turned away.

He thought about a general children's hospital in the bayous of Louisiana or in the back country of the Mississippi River Delta. He was projecting a probable cost of a million dollars to build the hospital and about three hundred thousand a year to maintain it. He hoped that, after it was built, it might be turned over to an order of nuns for its administration.

Danny and the Cardinal talked about his dream often. Danny also discussed it with another special friend, Abe Lastfogel, the man who had discovered Danny that stormy night in Chicago. Mr. Lastfogel was now head of the William Morris Agency and was considered the most influential man in the entertainment industry in the United States. He represented Danny and many other top artists from coast to coast.

One day he challenged Danny, "You keep talking about building a hospital. Are you really going to do it?"

Danny assured him that he was. Lastfogel then suggested that they form a committee, organize a board of directors and get started. The first meeting was held in his office. All who were at the meeting were close personal friends as well as being closely associated with Danny Thomas.

Besides Lastfogel there was Morris Stoller, the controller of the William Morris Agency; Maury Foladare, Danny's press agent and public relations representative; Paul Ziffren, Danny's attorney; Paul's brother, Leo Ziffren, also an attorney; Janet Roth, Danny's secretary; Eli Parker, Danny's business manager; Dr. Daniel H. Levinthal, nationally-known orthopedic surgeon, who was originally from Chicago; and Professor John Boles of Loyola University in Los Angeles..

This group formed the St. Jude Hospital Foundation of California at that meeting in 1951. Paul Ziffren drew up the legal papers necessary for Danny to start raising money officially for his dream.

One who attended that meeting says today that he thought the chances of accomplishing what Danny dreamed of were very remote — and he thought all who were there might have felt much the same way — but they all loved Danny and were behind him completely. What he wanted was what they wanted. They all gave of their time and talents then, as they still do, with no one ever receiving one penny of remuneration. With the exception of Eli Parker, who died in 1971, and Dr. Levinthal, who died in 1978, all those present at that first meeting are still actively involved with Danny Thomas and St. Jude Children's Research Hospital.

After the Foundation had been established, Danny reported to Cardinal Stritch that he had raised several thousand dollars toward the hospital. The Cardinal, somewhat amazed, asked him, "You're really determined to go through with this, aren't you?"

"Of course I am," Danny replied.

"Then it's time we figure out what kind of hospital you're going to build."

Where the hospital was to be located was never a question for Samuel Cardinal Stritch. He talked down Danny's idea of a remote area in the south, citing lack of transportation and of available doctors, along with many other problems the location might create.

And, he talked up Memphis, Tennessee. He gave Danny many reasons why it should be built there. Memphis had a great medical community that was centered around the University of Tennessee medical college. He went into great detail about the airlines, bus terminals and railroad station facilities as well as its convenience by automobile.

He ended his argument with, "Besides, it's my hometown."

Danny's answer to the last statement was, "Your Eminence, why didn't you just say so in the first place and you wouldn't have had to go through the dissertation?" Memphis was not actually the Cardinal's hometown — he was born in Nashville, Tennessee. But he called Memphis home since his first parish was located there. In 1911 he had gone to Memphis as assistant pastor of St. Patrick's church and was later to become its pastor. His brother was a priest in Memphis and the Cardinal had many friends there.

These friends included the family of John Ford Canale — a family who always entertained the Cardinal when he was in Memphis. In addition to Canale, the Cardinal told Danny that he should contact an attorney, Edward F. Barry. Mr. Barry was chairman of, or on the board of, several Memphis hospitals.

The Cardinal's advice to Danny, as Danny recalls it, was, "If Mr. Barry takes you on, you stay in Memphis and you will build your hospital. If he says, 'No, it's too much.' you just get on your Arabian steed and go someplace

"Most men dream dreams, but only a few see their dreams come true. From his promise grew a dream."

Left: Cardinal Stritch

else." According to Danny that someplace else would have been Chicago or Dallas. But a second choice was not necessary. Mr. Barry "took him on".

Ed Barry had been very active in hospital campaigns in the Memphis area. He had held one of the key positions in one of the first hospital drives ever conducted in the city. He had been approached and accepted a major responsibility in an effort to raise two million dollars in two separate drives of a million each for Baptist Memorial Hospital, the world's largest private hospital. Following this, he went on to help raise a substantial amount for Methodist Hospital. He had just agreed to help raise a million dollars to build a sizeable addition to St. Joseph Hospital when Danny contacted him.

He recalls having heard that "this fellow Thomas" had "made a statement to the effect that as an act of gratitude to what he accepted as intercession of St. Jude in the direction of his profession, that he would one day build him a shrine". When he heard this, Ed Barry had no idea that Danny and Cardinal Stritch would have plans for that shrine to be a hospital in Memphis and that he would be the most important person in the city in its realization.

Barry was invited to attend a meeting in Mayor Frank Tobey's office to discuss locating the hospital in Memphis. John Ford Canale, an attorney; Willard W. Scott, a banker; and Paul Malloy, author of a column "Dixie Dialing" that appeared in the Commercial Appeal, a Memphis newspaper, were also there. Representing Danny Thomas and the St. Jude Hospital Foundation of California was Sol Rubin, a member of the board of directors of the City of Hope Medical Center near Los Angeles, a friend of Danny's and a person who also had business interests in the Memphis area.

Following this meeting, Danny invited the participants to meet with him in California to discuss the hospital plans. In late February of 1955 Ed Barry, Bill Scott, Mayor Tobey and Paul Malloy made the trip. During the day they met members of Danny's family, they toured the movie studio and talked with several celebrity friends of Danny Thomas. Late in the afternoon they returned to Danny's house where he put a direct question to them, "Do you think the people of Memphis would like to have this hospital located in their city?"

The experience that Ed Barry had with hospitals gave him a very practical approach. He knew it was not enough to say that the city would like to have the hospital without first carefully studying the situation. He answered Danny's question with three questions of his own.

The first — was there a need? At that particular time leaders in Memphis were concerned about the building of unnecessary institutions, especially in the health care field.

The second addressed how the hospital would be maintained. The third was the amount of money that Danny expected them to raise in Memphis from Memphis citizens.

Visiting with Danny in Los Angeles and talking about his plans for his shrine to St. Jude are (from the left) Ed Barry; Mayor Frank Tobey; Danny Thomas; Sol Rubin, member of the St. Jude Hospital Foundation of California; and Willard Scott. Below: Dr. Lemuel Diggs

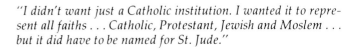

"I didn't want just a Catholic institution. I wanted it to represent all faiths . . . Catholic, Protestant, Jewish and Moslem . . . but it did have to be named for St. Jude."

The meeting broke up without addressing fully the first two questions, but the third was discussed. Danny asked if Memphis could raise a half million dollars. He and his St. Jude Hospital Foundation could raise a million and a half if Memphis could raise the half million.

The Memphians returned home to discuss the project with members of the community. Mr. Barry talked with several community leaders who questioned the need for another hospital built specifically to treat children. LeBonheur Children's Hospital had just been completed and it was felt that one children's hospital was sufficient for the community, especially since that one was reinforced by pediatric wings in all the major hospitals in Memphis.

At that time, Danny's plan was to build St. Jude Hospital as a general pediatric hospital. There did not seem to be much positive reaction to that idea, especially from members of the medical community.

But discussion continued back and forth between Memphis and California. A medical advisory committee was named in Memphis. Its members were Dr. Ralph O. Rychener, noted opthomologist who was president of the National Medical Foundation for Eye Care and would later be president of the Memphis and Shelby County Medical Society and the Tennessee State Medical Association; Dr. Gilbert J. Levy, Associate Professor of Pediatrics at the University of Tennessee; and Dr. Lemuel W. Diggs, Professor of Medicine at the University of Tennessee and head of the department of Hematology.

Dr. Diggs taught a class at the University of Tennessee in clinical pathology which included the study of leukemia and other blood diseases. He was highly qualified in this field and was the only doctor in Memphis at that time who was involved in the study of leukemia and sickle cell anemia.

In one of the meetings of the advisory committee Dr. Diggs suggested that, since no other hospital in Memphis really was equipped to care for children with catastrophic diseases, a research hospital devoted to the study of this type disease might be what was needed.

He and the other members of the committee believed that the only thing that would justify a hospital being built in Memphis, Tennessee with funds gathered from across the United States would be if the hospital served all children in the country. A research hospital that would share its information with other medical facilities across the United States would do this.

They preached the gospel of research and Danny Thomas listened. His shrine to St. Jude would be a research hospital for children with catastrophic diseases.

With this decision, the picture changed. The medical community and the staff at the medical school recognized the potential involved in the creation of a national research center. They noted that it would stimulate training in both research and clinical studies.

Practical businessmen looked at the hospital proposal with renewed interest. A national hospital would draw patients and staff from across the country and would be a definite asset to the city and its medical community.

It was now time to move ahead with plans to raise Memphis' share of the construction costs and to choose a site for the hospital that would be dedicated to the treatment of children with diseases that were, at that time, considered fatal in all instances.

Danny Thomas and members of the St. Jude Hospital Medical Advisory Board. From the left: Dr. William F. Mackey, Dr. Gilbert Levy, Danny Thomas, Dr. L. W. Diggs, Dr. Robert Raskind, Dr. Charles G. Allen, Jr., Dr. Ralph O. Rychener. Drs. Levy, Diggs and Rychener were the first Memphis doctors to be involved with the hospital in an advisory capacity.

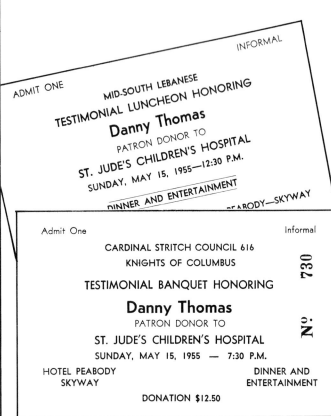

Clockwise: Invitation to the first Memphis fund-raising event for Danny's hospital. Tickets for the two events held on May 15, 1955. Danny holds two checks totalling $5,300.00 from the two events. Sharing his pleasure (from the left) Joe Gattas, George Mooney and Fred Gattas, all of Memphis.

Fun and Fund-raising

The first major fund-raising event held by the St. Jude Hospital Foundation of California had been staged in 1951 in a Chicago theater. It was the Midwest premiere of Danny Thomas' new film "I'll See You in My Dreams" with Doris Day. Samuel Cardinal Stritch was the honorary chairman of the event.

When Danny speaks of that night, he relates it to the number 51: "We raised $51,000 that night in 1951. It's funny how that number has haunted me for years. I catapulted out of the 5100 Club in Chicago — we collected $51,000 at our first major benefit — and St. Jude Hospital is built on Highway 51 in Tennessee."

Following the decision that St. Jude Hospital would be a research facility, and with a growing interest among the citizens of Memphis, it was decided that the time was right for a major fund-raising event in Memphis. Danny did not want it to be just a fund-raiser — he also wanted it to be a getting-acquainted affair. He planned a two-week stay in Memphis to introduce its populace to his dream and to invite them to help make the dream come true.

Mayor Frank Tobey issued an official proclamation declaring May 12 through May 22, 1955 as Danny Thomas Week. The proclamation urged the citizens of Memphis to "Acquaint themselves with Danny Thomas and his admirable hopes and aspirations for St. Jude Hospital".

On May 15, 1955 two events were held to kick off the week. Earlier in the year when Sol Rubin had visited Memphis as Danny's envoy, he had contacted Fred P. Gattas, owner of a catalog store in the city and a man who was active in business circles in the community. Gattas arranged for Rubin to speak at a luncheon of the Elks Club for Danny and his dream. And, Gattas became very interested in the project, volunteering to help in any way he could.

As a result of this involvement Fred Gattas was chairman for a luncheon that was held that May 15, sponsored by the Memphis Lebanese community. There were, at that time, about fifteen thousand people of Lebanese descent in the tri-state area of Tennessee, Arkansas and Mississippi. These were invited through their local and regional organizations to attend this luncheon given by the Memphis community in honor of Danny Thomas, their fellow Lebanese.

That same evening a dinner was sponsored by the Knights of Columbus. The two events raised a total of over five thousand dollars for Danny's dream. A Memphis businessman, Nat Buring, was to make the first major individual gift in Memphis with a pledge of two thousand dollars at the Knights of Columbus dinner.

The night of May 27 an outdoor benefit was planned in Crump stadium. Admission was on a "give-what-you-can" basis. It had been announced in local news articles and in Paul Malloy's "Dixie Dialing" column that two tickets would be sent on a first-come basis to anyone who sent in a contribution in any amount.

Fifteen thousand people packed the stadium to be entertained by such stars as Dinah Shore, Carmen Cavallaro, the Skylarks, the highest paid dance team in the world Darvas and Julia, singer Frank Parker from the Arthur Godfrey show, and Rusty Hamer who was then starring with Danny Thomas in the "Make Room for Daddy" television series.

All the stars donated their time. When Abe Lastfogel is asked how he and Danny got all the stars there he answers, "All we did was ask."

But Dr. Donald Pinkel, St. Jude's first medical director, adds another dimension to that statement when he speaks of Abe Lastfogel, "His word was law in show business." The stars were more than willing to accede to the "request" of Abe Lastfogel.

Others who participated in the concert also donated their time and talents. The Memphis Federation of Musicians furnished a concert orchestra under the direction of Memphian Noel Gilbert. Workers from the Park Commission constructed the stage. The ushers were all volunteers. The local Coca-Cola distributor provided the sound system.

Everything was "go" on the day of the big show . . . everything except the weather. In Memphis events scheduled during the month of May frequently run into weather problems. The annual Cotton Carnival is held each year in May and any native may be heard to mutter when discussing the weather, "Sure, it will rain . . . it's Cotton Carnival time."

Danny had been forewarned of this possibility and Memphians working with him on the event had suggested selecting an alternate site in case of rain. Danny's answer to all was, "Hush! St. Jude might hear you. It isn't going to rain."

The day of the event the forecast was for rain . . . a possible four inches. Danny recalls it this way: "That's when I got mad at St. Jude. St. Jude is a rough taskmaster. He doesn't help you until you get up to your nose in quicksand. I get so angry with him. I yell and scream at him."

"That day the strangest formation of clouds appeared. They were black and churning. You could not see. At three o'clock in the afternoon the lights were on all over the city. The men from the city park department were putting up bunting around the stage and lining it with plants."

"I called the Naval Air Station weather and they said four inches of rain was due any minute. I kept looking up at the clouds and I asked, "Why? What am I doing that's wrong? Is it wrong for me to be here? Is this not the place to build the hospital? There are going to be thousands of people coming to this benefit. These stars have flown in from everywhere to entertain . . ."

"I looked away and one of the workmen called out to me, 'Hey, Mr. T, take a look.' It was the craziest cloud formation I have ever seen in my life. The clouds just pulled apart and, so help me, it looked like there was a crescent moon with a star over it. And it stayed that way. It never moved."

"At the end of the show I walked out on the stage and asked, 'If any of you people here don't think that this project has been touched by the hand of God, I beg you to look up into the sky.' They did and they all applauded."

Top left: Arriving in Memphis for the big show. From the left: Carmen Cavallaro, Mrs. Cavallaro, Mrs. Dorothy Hamer, Abe Lastfogel, Mrs. Lastfogel, Danny Thomas, Rusty Hamer, Rose Marie Thomas, Sol Rubin and Mrs. Rubin. Far left: Danny arrives at the stadium for the show. Left: Dinah Shore and the Skylarks entertain the crowd.

"We had done about a two hour and twenty minute show and I said, 'Good night and God bless you!' The crowd headed for their cars. All of a sudden they started running, and, I hope to die, the minute they left the rain came down in a sheet!"

While Danny was in Memphis that May of 1955 he took one weekend to fly to New York for an appearance on Bert Parks' television show "Break the Bank".

Before he left he told Mayor Tobey that he planned to break the piggy banks of America for St. Jude. On the show that Sunday evening he asked each healthy child to break his or her piggy bank and send just one dollar to help him with his hospital.

The Memphis post office was inundated with mail. Virginia Bloesch, an executive with National Bank of Commerce, recalls that she was working in the downtown office of the bank and was one of those who opened the mail, read the letters and counted the money. "The letters just kept coming and coming ... we were so excited," she remembers today.

When Danny got off the plane in Memphis the day following the show his pockets were bulging with dollar bills that people on the streets of New York, at the New York Airport and on the airplane had pressed upon him.

The citizens of Memphis and the surrounding area rallied to support Danny and his dream. Fifty meter readers from the power company had a fund that they collected from a soft drink machine in their lunchroom. They had planned a party with the money but instead voted to turn over the five hundred dollars in the kitty to St. Jude Hospital. Suddenly, a party was not as important to them as the possibility of seeing the day that sick children would have the opportunity to become well children.

Sailors and Marines at Memphis Naval Air Station took up a collection and gave two thou-

Top left: One of Danny's first stops after arriving in Memphis was the Shrine School for Crippled Children where he visited with the children, parents and staff. Lower: Before he left Memphis by plane to appear on Bert Parks' Break the Bank show, Danny said that he was going to ask each child to give a dollar from his piggy bank for St. Jude Hospital. Jay Chapleau of Memphis gets into the spirit of the occasion by giving Danny his entire piggy bank!

sand dollars to the fund in honor of Danny and the tours that he had made with the U.S.O. to entertain troops during the war years. Danny made a trip to the base to thank them personally. He promised that he would tell the American people how "you fellows who are serving your country for peanuts dug deep to give to a hospital for underprivileged children".

After Danny's visit in 1955 there were very few people of any religious belief in Memphis and the mid-South area who had not heard the story of St. Jude and Danny's plans to build a hospital dedicated to the patron saint of the hopeless. One doctor recalls that "the Southern Baptists had known all about and liked St. Peter, but they'd never heard of this fellow, St. Jude,

before Danny."

The Dominican priests at historic St. Peter's church in downtown Memphis, just a few blocks from where the hospital would be built, erected a shrine in the right apse of their church to St. Jude Thaddeus. A part of the contributions at the shrine are still forwarded to the hospital to help with its research and treatment of children stricken with a catastrophic illness.

The hospital was becoming the realization of Danny's dream that "I didn't want the hospital to be a Catholic institution. I wanted it to represent all faiths . . . Catholic, Protestant, Jewish and Moslem . . . but it did have to be named for St. Jude." Memphis had taken Danny Thomas and his shrine to St. Jude to its heart.

Above: Danny Thomas embraces Mayor Tobey of Memphis after being publicly assured that Beale Avenue would once again be Beale Street. Above right: A few years later Danny visited Beale Street and played a little blues on W. C. Handy's trumpet for Matthew Thornton, unofficial mayor of Beale Street and some of its residents. Right: Danny tells Pamela Venson a little bit about Handy, Beale Street and his St. Jude Hospital that was under construction just a few blocks away.

Left: Elvis lends his talents to the 1957 show in his home town. Left center: Ed Barry rehearses Danny Thomas and Jane Russell backstage before the show. Bottom left: Singer Roberta Sherwood captures the attention of the crowd. Below: Flanked by Ed Barry on his left and John Ford Canale on his right, Danny displays the Mayor's proclamation declaring the day of the show as "Danny Thomas Day." Standing, from the left: Fred P. Gattas, Sol Rubin, Joe Gattas and Walter Popp. Rubin and Popp were traveling with Danny. Bottom right: Danny receives key to the city from Mayor Edmund Orgill and representatives of the city. From left clockwise: Dave Harsh, Don Mitchell, Fred G. Gattas, Sol Rubin, John Ford Canale, Danny, Henry Loeb, Mayor Orgill, John T. Dwyer, and Stanley Dillard.

Forging Ahead . . . by Inches

Two years passed. Danny continued to raise money through his St. Jude Hospital Foundation of California. Much of what he raised was from his own efforts, money that he had made and donated to the Foundation.

At the all-star show in Memphis in 1955 Danny had sung a song he called "Bring Back My Beale Street". He had always been interested in the blues and he talked about the blues and its origin in his night club acts. He still does.

On his arrival in Memphis he visited world-famous Beale Street where W.C. Handy had immortalized the blues. There he found, to his dismay, that the sign on that famous street read "Beale Avenue". Asking why, he discovered that years earlier a Memphis ordinance had been passed that standardized all east-west thoroughfares as avenues and all north-south ones as streets. Thus, Beale Street, running east from the Mississippi River, had become Beale Avenue officially.

The night before the show Danny sat down in his hotel room and wrote the song "Bring Back My Beale Street". He introduced it at the show and received an instant promise from Mayor Tobey that Beale Avenue would become Beale Street again — very soon!

Following the show, Danny had the song arranged and published. He recorded it and it was put on two thousand jukeboxes across the nation with a sticker stating that the proceeds were to be donated to St. Jude Hospital. This was one of the many commercial ventures that Danny entered into for the benefit of the hospital. For years, as spokesman for Maxwell House coffee, Danny's fee, amounting to hundreds of thousands of dollars, was donated to the hospital.

June of 1957 found Danny Thomas and another cast of all-star entertainers, including Jane Russell, back in Memphis for another show. Again, two tickets would be sent to anyone who made a donation, no matter what the amount. All Danny asked was that people give what they could and give from their hearts. This show was held in Russwood Park where the Memphis baseball team played their games.

Again it was outdoors. When Danny arrived in town he was handed a newspaper with a headline that read, "Rain predicted, but never fear, Danny's here". Others were not so sure of the weather, though. They were still to be convinced.

Dr. L.W. Diggs, the member of the Medical Advisory committee who had given the hospital its purpose — the study and treatment of childhood catastrophic diseases — recalls his experiences that evening.

"While I was at first drafted by the University to become involved in this project — one that seemed reasonable enough — I was still not overly enthusiastic and was reluctant to be deeply involved. That night in Russwood Park a public meeting was held to obtain funds in behalf of St. Jude Hospital. Various entertainers, including Elvis Presley, volunteered in order to attract a crowd. Mrs. Diggs and I dutifully bought tickets and went."

"The weather was threatening. It had been raining and there was a very black cloud in the west with occasional lightning flashes. A bad storm with wind and heavy rain seemed imminent. Soon after, the winds changed, the skies cleared and instead of a black and threatening cloud there was a bright evening star right over the area where the St. Jude Hospital would be built."

"That star was a natural phenomenon and had always been in its proper place at a proper time, but this time it was a symbol that told me something. After that, I suddenly became sure that the St. Jude cause was indeed worthy and should be supported."

"In order to see the Star of Hope that St. Jude offers one has to look up and look into the distance. It cannot be seen by looking down or by looking straight in front of you, or by allowing clouds to obscure its view."

For several years Danny Thomas had been raising money for his dream with only one visual aid — the architect's rendering of the proposed St. Jude Hospital. The design and plans had been donated by his friend, Paul Williams, a noted black architect.

Paul Williams grew up in Memphis, Tennessee. He was the son of a headwaiter at the famous Peabody Hotel. He moved to Los Angeles and became one of the world's outstanding architects. Williams achieved national recognition for his designs that included the Los Angeles International Airport, the Los Angeles County Court House and three buildings on the campus of the University of California. He designed Woodrow Wilson High School, Los Angeles' first high-rise school. He also was the architect for many of the major business buildings in the area as well as homes for hundreds of the world's most famous people.

Danny says, "I stole the plans from my dear friend, Paul Williams. He drew this hospital free. This man has designed some of the most beautiful hotels in Las Vegas and some of the most handsome institutions in Los Angeles."

"He designed the hospital in the shape of a five-pointed star. The insignia of St. Jude is a five-pointed star! Williams insisted he never knew this fact. Some people call this a nice coincidence. I call it the hand of God pushing Williams' pencil."

Paul Williams said that it was the most satisfying building that he had ever created because of the work that was being done there.

Danny presented a problem to the Memphis steering committee that summer of 1957. It had become very difficult for him to raise money with just a picture. He felt that he had to have "something coming out of the ground", concrete evidence that a structure was indeed being built.

Once again the committee raised the question of maintenance. Some of the Memphis leaders were afraid that Memphis would be left with a white elephant that it would have to maintain. They kept asking the steering committee, "How are you going to get the money to maintain the hospital?"

Ed Barry, once again, asked Danny a question that he had asked before. "Why do we say that we are going to operate a free hospital? Let's say that we will operate it with as little cost to the patient as possible."

Danny's answer was the same as before. No one was going to pay. And he asked for time until the fall of that year, 1957. He would then have the answer for funding the maintenance of the hospital. There was over a million and a half dollars in the bank to build the building. Now he must find a way to meet its daily needs.

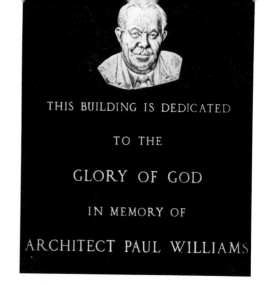

THIS BUILDING IS DEDICATED

TO THE

GLORY OF GOD

IN MEMORY OF

ARCHITECT PAUL WILLIAMS

"The Star of St. Jude is a symbol that human intelligence, initiative and drive, and the use of the talents that we have have been endowed with and the resources we have at our command, will be utilized to benefit children who are in desperate need. I know of no cause that is more challenging, that has a greater purpose, or a greater future."

Left: From the start, friends and associates of Danny Thomas believed in his dream and appeared with him to raise funds to make it a reality. One of those was Jack Benny. Top: The plaque that one sees in the outer lobby of the hospital pays tribute to the designer of the "Star of Hope." Center: At a dinner in his honor, Paul Williams, flanked by Danny Thomas, accepts the "thank you" of the crowd.

"What I want to see is something in which we can all take part, because in helping children we reaffirm man's faith in man and only when that is done can we possibly reaffirm man's faith in God."

Above: Danny appeals to his people to assist him in the support of his dream.

Danny's People Rally Behind Him

During the time that Danny was raising money for his dream with a picture, a prayer and a great deal of hope and faith, he was chosen by the Arabic-speaking people of America as the Lebanese of the Century.

At the time that he received the award he asked, "Why me?" The answer was that he had been honored because of his success in the theatrical business and also because he was a person who was not ashamed of his heritage.

He could not understand why a person should receive an award of such stature for those reasons alone. He wanted to really earn the recognition. He now felt that he had found the way that he could earn this award.

He would do this by uniting his contemporaries, the second and third generation Americans — sons and daughters of Arabic-speaking immigrants who had come to this new world seeking a better life for their sons and daughters and generations to come. He would unite his people in the support of a single cause — to provide the funds necessary to maintain his dream, St. Jude Children's Research Hospital.

The Arabic-speaking Americans were spread throughout the country from coast to coast and they had formed many local and regional organizations and clubs that raised funds for both local and regional charities. They also contributed to all nationally recognized charities. But they had never before organized as a group in the support of one single effort.

That summer of 1957, Danny telephoned a dozen or more of the Arabic-speaking community leaders across the country. He told them that he wanted to meet with a representative group of leaders of people of Syrian/Lebanese ethnic background. He had a proposal to make to them.

All those he spoke with were invited to join him at a luncheon at the Sheraton Park Hotel in Washington, D.C. After the luncheon Danny showed them Paul Williams' drawing of the hospital he planned to build in Memphis, Tennessee.

He explained that he wanted it to be a research hospital and that it would serve children from everywhere, of all races and creeds, and at no cost to the child's family. He told them that he had most, and could get the rest, of the money needed to construct the hospital building and equip it. But he needed an organization that would assure the funds for the day-to-day maintenance.

He had come to them, his people, because never in the history of this country had people of their ethnic background joined together as a group to honor their forefathers who had come to America seeking a new world for their children. Nor had they done anything as a group to say "thank you" to America for letting their forefathers come to this country, establish themselves in the business and professional community and raise their children to enjoy the full benefits the country had to offer.

Danny pointed out to those who had met with him that their ancestors were unknown in America. He proposed that by their deeds in maintaining St. Jude Hospital their forefathers would be honored and would be known.

He asked if they would, in the name of their forefathers, assume the responsibility of raising approximately three hundred thousand dollars a year to meet the expenses of the hospital. In 1957, that seemed like a great deal of money to those who had come to meet with him. Some were pessimistic. Some asked why he did not go

———————————

"The Star of Hope that will hang over St. Jude is the star of hope for children who have catastrophic diseases now considered incurable and their families. It may not be the same star that shone over Bethlehem one wintry night but it is the same kind of star and carries the same kind of hope."

———————————

Left: The three who put it all together on October 10, 1957. From the left: Michael F. Tamer, Danny Thomas and Dr. Lemuel W. Diggs.

to the Eastern churches or through similar religious groups for his support.

Danny's answer to this was that he wanted no specific religious group to sponsor the hospital. He wanted it to be completely free of religious influence — completely non-sectarian.

The meeting adjourned after Danny had extracted a promise that each man present would give the proposal thought, take the idea back to his organization and see what might be done.

After the meeting Danny met privately with one man. Michael F. Tamer, president of the Midwest Federation of Syrian Lebanese American Clubs, had been the most enthusiastic of those at the meeting. Danny asked him if he would spearhead the project. Mike agreed to give it his best effort.

This meeting was the beginning of a partnership and a deep friendship between Danny Thomas and Mike Tamer that was to continue for seventeen years until Mike's death at the age of 70 in November of 1974.

A man of his word, Mike called a meeting of a smaller group in his hometown of Indianapolis, Indiana a few weeks later. Those who attended responded to Mike's forceful persuasion and agreed to form an organization, completely separate from any other existing Arabic-speaking group.

A meeting was planned to be held in Chicago at the Morrison Hotel on October 10, 1957 and a call went out nationally for their people to attend this meeting.

One hundred responded to the invitation and they listened to Dr. L.W. Diggs outline the proposed hospital as both a research center and a treatment center for children suffering from catastrophic diseases. They heard Danny as he spoke of his plans and dreams for the hospital.

And they formed ALSAC — American Lebanese Syrian Associated Charities, Inc. A program was outlined for organizing a nationwide network of supporting chapters and the group unanimously adopted St. Jude Hospital as its first official project.

At the same meeting officers were elected, an executive board was created and a national director and executive secretary were named.

The officers were:

Danny Thomas, President

Judge Joseph Rashid, 1st Vice-President (Detroit, Michigan)

B.D. Eddie, 2nd Vice-President (Oklahoma

𝕻reamble

TO THE CONSTITUTION

OF

AMERICAN LEBANESE SYRIAN ASSOCIATED CHARITIES

ONE HUNDRED AND ONE YEARS AGO, *our people began a migration to the blessed shores of these United States of America, seeking the freedoms and opportunities won for us by our founding fathers.*

SINCE THAT TIME, *we have increased greatly in number and have been enjoying the protection of the "Bill of Rights," yet we have never done anything as a body to justify our use of these rights. True, many of our people have distinguished themselves as good Americans and have risen to lofty heights in their particular lines of endeavor; but we have never really distinguished ourselves in a body. We have never united on a national basis in a common American cause.*

THEREFORE: *we who are proud of our heritage; having met in Washington, D. C., in June, Nineteen Hundred and Fifty-Seven, then again in Indianapolis, Indiana, in June, Nineteen Hundred and Fifty-Seven, and now in Chicago, Illinois, on this Tenth Day of October, in the Year of Our Lord, Nineteen Hundred and Fifty-Seven; have formed a non-profit, non-sectarian, charitable corporation titled ALSAC (American-Lebanon-Syrian Associated Charities) dedicated to the parable of the "Good Samaritan," to love and care for our neighbor, regardless of color or creed. This dedication shall manifest itself in the maintenance of St. Jude Hospital, Memphis, Tennessee, which, in turn, is dedicated to the cure of leukemia and related blood diseases in children, absolutely free. In so doing, we shall serve God and Our Country and we shall serve the good names of our fathers and mothers who made possible our birth in America, the land of the free.*

WE, *at long, long, last, shall take our rightful place in this community of nationalities —standing proudly with our heads held high in the knowledge that we have earned the right to perpetuate the name of our heritage and maintain our reputation as unquestioned good American Citizens.*

WITH THESE THOUGHTS *engraved in my mind and my heart, I shall call upon that powerful patron, St. Jude Thaddeus, to obtain for our organization the blessings of "Our Heavenly Father."*

To this Preamble I hereby dedicate my life and affix my signature.

Danny Thomas, President

AIDING LEUKEMIA STRICKEN AMERICAN CHILDREN

City, Oklahoma)

Dr. Naif Basile, 3rd Vice-President (New York, New York)

LaVonne Rashid, Recording Secretary Indianapolis, Indiana)

James Haboush, Treasurer (Chicago, Illinois)

Michael F. Tamer, National Executive Director (Indianapolis, Indiana)

Honorary Presidents were:

Metropolitan Antony Bashir, Archbishop of New York and all North America for the Syrian-Antiochian Orthodox Church

Chorbishop Michael Abraham from Michigan City, Indiana of the Maronite Rite

Rt. Rev. Monsignor Elias B. Skaff from Brooklyn, New York of the Melkite Rite.

The Executive Board consisted of the officers, the National Executive Director and more than a hundred members of the Board of Trustees from twenty-seven states.

Most of those who became involved with this new organization based their optimism in accepting so great a challenge on the energy, drive and dedication of Mike Tamer. He had agreed to take a year from his business and devote it to the organization of ALSAC — all at his own personal expense.

Mike's people truly loved him. They knew that the combined personal magnetism of Tamer and Thomas would convince their people that they really did have something to contribute to this country and that they really were a very important ethnic group in America.

Because their fathers had come to a new land, had struggled (some as peddler merchants), survived and educated their children, these, their children, were now to show their appreciation of this effort. As Danny had told them over and over, "By our deeds they shall be known."

ALSAC was incorporated in November of 1957 in the state of Illinois as a non-profit organization. Its stated purposes were:

1. To receive funds for the maintenance of St. Jude Hospital in Memphis, Tennessee, a national institution dedicated to the care, cure and research of leukemia and related blood diseases in children, and care, cure and research of all other diseases afflicting mankind.

2. To foster and promote among Arabic speaking people and others: Civic; historic; partriotic; and benevolent activities.

3. To aid and assist in charitable causes without regard to race, creed or color.

4. To acquire, maintain, invest, reinvest and deal in such real and personal property as may be necessary for the transaction of its business and the accomplishment of the purposes for which it was formed.

5. This organization shall be a non-political, non-sectarian and non-profit organization.

Mike Tamer was the owner of a very successful wholesale tobacco and candy business in Indianapolis, Indiana. A small office at his business was set aside to be used as the office of ALSAC.

Mike asked LaVonne Rashid, who had been elected Recording Secretary of ALSAC if she would take a year, the same year he had dedicated, to help him on a full time, volunteer basis. Like Danny, LaVonne Rashid had made a vow to St. Jude and had not, as yet, fulfilled it. She decided that this might be the best way to fulfill this vow.

She moved into the small office that contained a desk, a typewriter and a small file cabinet. There were no funds, of course, for operating expenses so she used every method possible to keep from spending money. The files from those

Top right: Mike Tamer at his desk in the temporary ALSAC office. Left: The Preamble to the ALSAC Constitution, written by Danny Thomas, expresses his hopes and dreams — for his people and for his hospital.

Left: One of the many direct mail appeals cranked out on the used ditto machine by LaVonne Rashid, (below).

early days show that carbons of letters sent out were made on the backs of incoming letters and "junk mail" that arrived in the office.

LaVonne was able to acquire a ditto machine, a hand-operated model, from a local minister. From this she cranked out the first newsletters that were to go out across the country. When they were ready, her mother and Mike Tamer's wife, Marie, would take dinner for four down to the office. After dinner all four would work to assemble the newsletters for mailing.

One of the first mailings asked each Arabic-speaking person to contribute just five dollars to ALSAC. This was followed by a mailing that offered Life memberships at a hundred dollars each.

While LaVonne was holding down the fort at the office, Mike Tamer was on the road preaching the gospel of St. Jude to his people. He traveled the length and breadth of the country talking with people, cajoling them, sometimes screaming at them — with love — to support this cause that he was so dedicated to.

As one of the early "believers" describes it, he "persuaded the non-believers by debating the merits of St. Jude's cause amongst gatherings of our people with tears streaming down his cheeks in between the 'forever present cigar' in his mouth".

He worked at organizing chapters in various cities and he appointed ten regional directors to go out into their territories and organize new chapters. The regional directors all travelled at their own expense, as did Mike Tamer.

When Danny could take time from his television schedule, he and Mike would hit the road by automobile, meeting each day with a group in a different city. Some days they would even

Top left: Emile Hajar, Commander of the N.G. Beram Veterans Association, the first ALSAC chapter to be chartered. Mr. Hajar has been a member of the Board of Directors since 1962. Below: Billboard announcing Danny Thomas appearance in Kansas City, Missouri in 1959. Bottom: Mike Tamer, playing for St. Jude Hospital with encouragement from Danny Thomas, at a Las Vegas night party in St. Louis, Missouri.

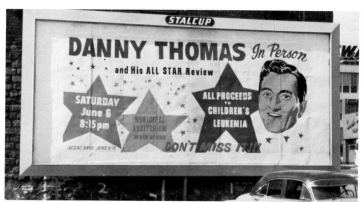

make two meetings in two different cities or towns.

And, wherever their people gathered, after the meetings and business sessions were over, there would be poker games until the wee hours of the morning. Mike and Danny would join these games and Danny tells that Mike would start drawing for the house and, by early morning, everyone would be broke but St. Jude. Mike used these winnings to cover some of his expenses in wining and dining prospective workers or donors. He never presented an entertainment chit to the ALSAC organization for payment.

At the 1958 ALSAC convention Mike Tamer reported that he had visited forty cities in the past year — some of them as many as five times. More than 142 chapters had been formed in 35 states and $159,492.17 had been raised during the year.

The first chapter to be chartered was the N.G. Beram Veterans Association of Boston, Massachusetts. It is almost prophetic that it should be so since this organization had been involved with Danny more than five years before in a major fund-raising effort for his hospital.

In 1952 when Danny was appearing on the night club circuit at the Latin Quarter in Boston, he told newspaper interviewers about the dream he had of building a hospital. They asked if he would hold a fund-raising show in Boston. Danny assured them that he would if his people, the Arabic-speaking members of the community, would be included in the planning.

One of those contacted was Emile H. Hajar, then Commander of the N.G. Beram Veterans Association. He agreed to help and plans were made for the show to be held at the Boston Garden in September of that year.

The show headlined Danny Thomas and included his fellow entertainers Perry Como, Eddie Fisher, Zero Mostel, Red Buttons, Patti Page and Helen O'Connell, among others. It was a sell-out and raised $64,000 for Danny's dream.

And, it was the first time that an organization of Danny's people worked to support his cause. It was only right that this organization should have the honor of being the first chapter to be chartered in the ALSAC organization.

Before the 1958 convention Danny had asked Mike to stay on with ALSAC as its national director. He was really asking Mike to give up his business and devote full time to his dream.

Mike agreed to do it for one more year — it was always just "one more year".

At the convention, Mike pointed out the need for office equipment, supplies, secretarial help and campaign materials. He asked for an operating budget of $25,000 for the next year.

He got it, and LaVonne Rashid was put on the payroll as the first employee of ALSAC. Later, Sadie Shikany, who had been working for some time on a voluntary basis, was to join the small staff as bookkeeper.

The original members of ALSAC were Americans of Arabic-speaking descent whose parents, like Amos Jacob's parents, had emigrated from Lebanon, Syria or their neighboring nations . . . and included all faiths whether Eastern Orthodox, Catholic or Moslem.

LaVonne Rashid expressed the hopes of all members of ALSAC when she wrote an article for the Star, a Los Angeles Lebanese community newspaper, in October of 1957. It read, in part:

"Danny Thomas has entrusted the welfare of St. Jude Hospital to us. We are charged with the crusade of man's humanity to man. Guard it well, we must, lest in failing, we find ourselves covered with the quicksands of non-entity from which there can be no hope of arising."

Guard it well they did and, after the organization was well-established and funds were assured for the operation of the hospital for its early years, the people of ALSAC opened the organization to share with Americans all across the country regardless of race, religion or national origin. All were invited to participate in the support of Danny's hospital and ALSAC also became the symbol for Aiding Leukemia Stricken American Children.

"The ALSAC-St. Jude project has emerged as a non-sectarian democratic organization which in many ways typifies the real spirit of that self-same God of all mankind — Christian, Jewish, Moslem, Catholic and Eastern Orthodox. It had to be that way."

The Dream Becomes a Reality

With the organization of ALSAC assuring that funds would be available for maintenance of the hospital, the last remaining hurdle seemed to have been cleared. The Memphis steering committee moved ahead to secure the land for the hospital. All were in agreement that it should be located, as Cardinal Stritch had suggested, near the Medical Center and the University of Tennessee Medical School.

Ed Barry and John Ford Canale had hoped that the hospital could be located near St. Joseph Hospital and that the Sisters of St. Francis, who owned and operated St. Joseph, could serve as administrators for St. Jude. Both men served on the Lay Advisory Board of St. Joseph and had been involved in many discussions as to how the best possible working relationship might be effected.

Other pressures were also exerted from members of the medical community in Memphis. One evening, when Cardinal Stritch was visiting in Memphis and dining with the Canale family, another friend of the Canales dropped in to talk with him. He was Dr. John Shea, world-renowned Memphis specialist in diseases of the ear. He was trying to enlist the Cardinal's support for having Danny's hospital built as a pediatric wing of St. Joseph Hospital.

This had been mentioned before but the Cardinal knew that Danny was determined that his hospital be a separate entity. Only in that way could he feel assured that it would be available to children of all races and religions and at no cost to the families of the children treated.

Danny did agree with Barry and Canale that the Sisters of St. Francis would indeed be able administrators for the hospital and discussions and correspondence went back and forth with both the sisters in Memphis and the mother house in Mishawaka, Indiana.

Danny Thomas and the realization that others shared his dream (Far left). Left: Danny Thomas lights fire to start the clearing of the property where his hospital will be built. Lower left: He then helps the firemen put the fire out. Right: Very pleased with the results.

The steering committee was in favor of a seventeen-acre site directly adjacent to St. Joseph Hospital. The land was owned by the Memphis Housing Authority and was a part of the urban renewal program. This particular site had not been previously cleared because a decision had not been reached as to the route of the new east-west expressway. Where the expressway would go was to depend on the site selected for the new Tennessee-Arkansas bridge that would cross the Mississippi River just north of downtown Memphis.

Mayor Tobey had wanted the City of Memphis to donate the land for the hospital, but there was no land that belonged to the city that was available in the right area. And, it was not legally possible for the city to donate land that belonged to the Memphis Housing Authority.

An engineer, working with maintenance crews from St. Joseph Hospital, cut down trees and cleared enough of the land to get a line of sight and set corner stakes to show how the building would contour to the land. Danny wanted to see exactly where the points of the star would be located.

Pleased with what they saw, a decision was made to move forward and secure the site. On November 2, 1958 Danny Thomas lighted a symbolic fire to begin the clearing of the property.

This was followed by a ground-breaking ceremony where a specially constructed spade, blessed in accordance with Jewish, Roman Catholic and Protestant beliefs, was used. Participating in the ceremony with Danny was Rabbi James Wax of Temple Israel in Memphis; Monsignor J. Harold Shea, administrator of Sacred Heart Catholic Church in Memphis and Dean of West Tennessee; and Dr. Donald Henning, rector of Calvary Episcopal Church in Memphis.

Once again, the sun shone on a Danny Thomas-St. Jude endeavor. All who attended remarked that it was a very beautiful day even though it was November.

At last, Danny's dream was under way — seven years after he launched his campaign to raise funds for the construction of the "shrine to St. Jude" and one year after the formation of ALSAC.

One month after the ground-breaking, the first research grant was made to ALSAC by Plough, Inc., a Memphis-based drug and cosmetic firm. This enabled St. Jude Hospital to begin its research program even before its hospital building was completed. The ten thousand dollar grant was given to Dr. L.W. Diggs for the continuation of his work on sickle cell anemia and other related research that was being conducted in his laboratories at the University of Tennessee.

Dr. Diggs used the funds to hire a staff to assist with the research program. He, himself, served without remuneration from the grant monies.

His first report to ALSAC in 1959, after the first year of research, consisted of a three-page double-spaced typewritten study covering:
1. Clinical testing of new drugs for treatment of malignant diseases
2. Hemolytic anemia caused by drugs
3. Coagulation studies
4. Study of crises in sickle cell disease
5. Activities of Dr. Gerald Plitman. Dr. Plitman had been employed on a part-time basis to assist with the initiation of research activities; to help in the development of special techniques, in the training of residents and in the development of hospital plans.

It was a brief report but an auspicious one in the history of the hospital. For the past twenty

Top: Danny was welcomed at the Memphis Airport the day before the groundbreaking by (from the left) Nat Buring, Monsignor Merlin F. Kearney and Dr. Gilbert Levy. Center: The shovel used in the groundbreaking is presented to Danny at an ALSAC convention. Above: Sisters of St. Francis from neighbor St. Joseph Hospital join in the ceremonies. Right: Blessing of the specially constructed three part shovel by (from the left) Rabbi James A. Wax, Rt. Rev. Msgr. J. Harold Shea, and Rev. Donald Henning. Also "helping" is an unidentified neighborhood child.

years the report to ALSAC and the members of the Board of Governors on the studies done the previous year has grown with each issue, both in scientific achievements and in the number of pages it takes to relate them. The past year's Scientific Annual Report was a hundred and sixty-four page printed and bound volume!

While research was being conducted in temporary quarters at the University of Tennessee, work was beginning at the construction site.

The firm of Paul R. Williams, F.A.I.A. & Associates, was retained as the architect and the man who was to represent the Los Angeles firm on the St. Jude project was Claude H. Coyne, executive vice-president. He was to be personally involved in all phases of the project and would spend many days in Memphis before its completion.

In September of 1959, an agreement was signed with the local architectural firm of Mahan and Shappley. They were to provide input of information particular to the Memphis area and work closely with the Los Angeles firm. Arnold Shappley, Jr. was assigned to represent the Memphis firm.

One feature that was incorporated in the plans for the hospital was extremely unusual for Memphis at that time. When the Los Angeles engineers arrived in the area to review the soil conditions, the general strata and the topography of the site, they very quickly were alerted to something that most Memphians were not aware of. They found that Memphis was located in a high-risk earthquake fault zone, a Zone 3 area that could expect as powerful an earthquake as is probable in the United States — on a par with the San Francisco area. The New Madrid quake, centered just north of the Memphis area, that occurred in 1811 and 1812 (a total of three major quakes) is considered to be the most violent in the history of the United States.

Memphis building codes did not call for earthquake-resistant construction but, on the advice of the Los Angeles architects, St. Jude was the first building in Memphis to be built in conformance with the uniform building code to resist Zone 3 earthquake damage. Since St. Jude Hospital was completed, several other hospitals, a medical building, a county justice complex and several government buildings have been constructed to be earthquake-resistant.

The first building contract that was signed was

ST. JUDE HOSPITAL
GROUND BREAKING CEREMONIES

●

JACKSON AVE. & LAUDERDALE ST.

SUNDAY, NOVEMBER 2, 1958

2 P. M

MEMPHIS, TENNESSEE

PROGRAM

Master of Ceremonies	Edward F. Barry
Star Spangled Banner	Admiral's Band NATTC Millington
Invocation	Rt. Rev. Msgr. J. Harold Shea, V. F. Dean of West Tennessee Diocese of Nashville
Introduction of Guests	Edward F. Barry
Remarks	M. F. Tamer National Executive Director-ALSAC
Remarks	Rev. Donald Henning, Rector Calvary Episcopal Church
Welcome	Edmund Orgill, Mayor
Response	Danny Thomas
Address	Mr. Albert M. Cole, Administrator Housing & Finance Authority
Benediction	Rabbi James A. Wax Temple Israel
Breaking of Ground	Rabbi James A. Wax Rev. Donald Henning Rt. Rev. Msgr. J. Harold Shea Danny Thomas

with Hugh Dancy Excavation Company for site work. The amount was $25,000 and the work began in January of 1960.

In June of 1960 the construction contract was awarded to Southern Builders of Memphis. The amount was just under two and a half million dollars — $2,399,999.00. Ed Barry remembers it well. When the bids for construction came in he and Danny were reviewing them in a room at the Claridge Hotel. His calculations told him that they were about $900,000 short of being able to meet the bid.

Danny, on hearing the bad news, told him, "O.K. I'll take $400,000 and you take $500,000. We'll get it." And he flew back to Los Angeles to raise his share.

Barry reviewed the bids again, and determined that they would actually need an additional million and a quarter rather than the $900,000. He wrote Danny and then set out to raise Memphis' share.

The sale of the land to St. Jude Hospital was also finalized in the summer of 1960. The price paid to the Memphis Housing Authority was $132,118.

When ALSAC was formed its members had been assured by Danny Thomas that they would be called upon for the operational and maintenance funds only and that they would not be asked to get involved with the construction costs. They were not asked, but unsolicited funds did come to Ed Barry from the ALSAC organization. He recalls two checks, each in the amount of $200,000, that were sent to him to apply against the construction costs. In just over two years ALSAC was actively involved in a variety of fund-raising projects in preparation for the day the hospital would open its doors.

In looking back over the five years between the beginning of the drive to raise funds in 1955 until the actual construction began in 1960, one might wonder if there was a sense of frustration and despair in the minds and hearts of those who were so actively involved. Most believed, to the contrary, that the delay worked for the good of the hospital.

All planning and establishing of policy for the hospital depended totally upon volunteer workers. Many had freely given of their time and talent without compensation. But these same people were busy people, and often they were not able to give this project they were so dedicated to as much concentrated time as they

"I'm northern born and I've always heard about the slowpokes in the south but I never saw folks move as fast in the interest of a good cause as they do in Memphis."

"We, in Memphis, are going to give you our support 199%. We have faith in Danny Thomas and we all have faith in God. St. Jude Hospital cannot and will not fail."

Above: The professionals begin to clear the site with a little help from a friend with a very personal interest in the work. Right: Official signing of $2,399,999.00 construction contract by (from the left) Danny Thomas, Ed Barry and builder Harry Bloomfield. Checking over their shoulder to be sure they got it right, Architect Claude Coyne, Paul Williams' representative for the project (left) and Mike Tamer, Executive Director of ALSAC (right).

IN WITNESS WHEREOF the parties hereto have executed this Agreement, the day and year first above written.

ST. JUDE HOSPITAL INC., OF MEMPHIS, TENNESSEE

Danny Thomas

Founder
Date June 9, 1960

UTHERN BUILDERS INC., OF TENNESSEE
General Contractor
Date June 9, 1960

Edward J Barry

President

Harry Bloomfield

President

Below: Brochure that was used for earliest fund raising. Right, top: Early pledge card. Right, bottom: First full color brochure used to solicit funds for construction.

I Promised GOD

"Help me to find my place in life," I said, "and I will build you a shrine; a shrine where the poor, the helpless and the hopeless may come for comfort and aid."

I was one of these and He heard.

ng many
955 and
s of the
dation's
al Mem-
al loca-
Sam el
of the

of all
initial
de the
kemia

mber
n the
phis,

ning
ated
ital

... Jude Hospital Foundation, along
of nation wide friends and generous benefactors,

the broken earth symbolized a dream long in the making. It means the beginning of what eventually will become one of the nation's best equipped and most efficiently staffed research and treatment centers for childhood diseases such as leukemia.

St. Jude Hospital is pledged to the placing of NO restrictions on the acceptance and treatment of patients with children being welcomed from anywhere as long as the need for the hospital's service is indicated and as hospital capacity will permit.

Through the Foundation's untiring efforts, through diligent research and most modern facilities, as well as through contributions for establishing additional medical fellowships for further study, the hope aimed at eventual eradication of this child-killing disease is prayerfully anticipated.

Conveniently located on a plot of land donated by the citizens of Memphis, St. Jude Hospital is the design of Paul R. Williams, renowned nationally known architect. Featuring functional architecture and popular radial spoke-type design, the hospital has a number of wings emanating from a central medical "hub headquarters."

Prominent in the foyer will be a pair of wall plaques memorializing the late Samuel Cardinal Stritch and Mr. Thomas—two men whose faith and vision presage a new and wonderful achievement in man's compassion for the health and well-being of all children of God.

STAR OF ⭐ ST. JUDE

DEAR DANNY

COUNT ME IN FOR_____ DOLLARS $_____

TO HELP BUILD THE **ST. JUDE HOSPITAL** FOR CHILDREN IN MEMPHIS, TENN.

I SHALL PAY THIS PLEDGE AS FOLLOWS:_____

_____

PLEASE MAIL TO
IVAN D. HARRIS
ST. JUDE HOSPITAL FOUNDATION
P. O. BOX 357
MEMPHIS, TENN.

_____
NAME

_____
ADDRESS

FIRM OR INDIVIDUAL

SOLICITOR

PHONE NUMBER

"the star of hope for stricken children..."

would have liked. Thus, the time lag worked to an advantage ... they were able to give the necessary time because the demand for it was spread over a period of years.

An added advantage was that members of the Building Committee of the Memphis Steering Committee, with John T. Dwyer as chairman, were able to visit other hospitals across the country including the City of Hope Medical Center in the Los Angeles area, the Jimmy Fund in Boston, and research centers in Baltimore; Washington, D.C.; Chicago; Houston; Salt Lake City and New York City. From knowledge gained by touring these facilities and talking with key personnel the members of the committee were able to help plan a more effective hospital building.

The time lapse also allowed ALSAC to become well organized and to achieve a sound financial basis. Guaranteed maintenance placed St. Jude Hospital in a much better bargaining position in obtaining top staff personnel. Some of the first medical people that members of the steering committee had talked with from across the country had felt that there might be some hesitation on the part of top scientists to leave positions with secure institutions to take positions with a hospital whose continued maintenance could only be considered nebulous.

Between 1955 and 1960 there were three separate groups involved with the hospital project. Danny Thomas and the St. Jude Hospital Foundation of California were still raising money for the construction of the hospital. The Memphis Steering Committee was raising Memphis' share of the construction funds, as well as selecting the site, supervising construction plans and a myriad of other tasks its members had taken upon their shoulders.

The Memphis Steering Committee consisted of Ed Barry, chairman; John Ford Canale, vice-chairman; Fred P. Gattas, secretary; W.W. Scott, treasurer; John T. Dwyer, building committee chairman; and George Sisler, publicity. Honorary members were Dr. Ralph O. Rychener, Nat Buring, Paul Malloy and Mayor Frank Tobey, who would not live to see the hospital completed.

The ALSAC organization was raising funds for the maintenance of the hospital once it was opened. They had planned their third national convention to be held in Memphis in October of 1960.

This seemed a good time to develop a more structured organizational plan.

A meeting was held on October 7, 1960 to form a Board of Governors for the hospital and to elect an Executive Committee. The Board of Governors was to consist of Danny Thomas, Maury Foladare, Abe Lastfogel, Dr. Daniel H. Levinthal, Morris Stoller and Paul Ziffren from the St. Jude Foundation of California; Edward F. Barry, John Ford Canale, John T. Dwyer, Fred P. Gattas, W.W. Scott and George Sisler of the Memphis Steering Committee; Anthony R. Abraham, Dr. Naef K. Basile, John Bourisk, Albert Joseph, George Simon, Emile Reggie, Elias Chalhub, Dr. Thomas Boutrous, William F. Farha, Mrs. Mitchell Forzley and Michael F. Tamer of ALSAC; Dr. L.W. Diggs and Dr. Gilbert Levy representing the Shelby County Medical Association; and Sister Mary Alfreda O.S.F. and Sister Mary Stephanina O.S.F. representing the Order of the Sisters of St. Francis.

Those who were already serving as officers of the Memphis Steering Committee were elected to serve as officers. They were Edward F. Barry, president; W.W. Scott, treasurer; and Fred P. Gattas, secretary.

Each group appointed its own representatives to serve on the Executive Committee. It was to consist of Edward F. Barry as Chairman; Danny Thomas, Sister Mary Alfreda, Dr. Gilbert J. Levy, W.W. Scott, Michael F. Tamer, Fred P. Gattas and Emile A. Reggie.

Two days later the Board of Governors met to discuss the search for a medical director for the hospital. In that meeting there was a marked difference of opinion among the doctors who were members of the Board. In dispute was whether the director should be a pediatrician or a hematologist.

Dr. Levy and Dr. Diggs both felt that the director should be a pediatrician, well rounded in scientific medicine — preferably someone who would demonstrate a combination of pediatrics and hematology. Dr. Basile presented a report that he had prepared after consultation with experts from Cornell Medical Center and two leading European universities, the University of Paris and Munich University.

This report stated that preference should be given to a man who was a hematologist, not a pediatrician. He should also be relatively young and well-trained — the report continued — familiar with all aspects of research and treatment of leukemia and allied diseases. He should be a man of vision, administration, capably aggressive and hard working. In one word — a leader.

With these conflicting positions taken by the medical members of the Board, the Board itself became divided in its opinion. After much discussion, at times quite heated, agreement was finally reached with a resolution appointing a search committee of five members that would screen applicants before referring them to the Executive Committee for personal interviews. The committee was to consist of Drs. Levy, Diggs and Basile along with Ed Barry and Mike Tamer. It was to search for either a qualified hematologist or a pediatrician-hematologist.

The Board also took the position that the director would not be involved in fund-raising for the hospital nor would he be considered a public relations representative for it.

At the same meeting Sister Henrita from the order of the Sisters of St. Francis was appointed Administrator, climaxing the months of discussion that had taken place among Danny Thomas, Ed Barry, John Ford Canale and the Sisters of St. Francis. Danny's hospital would be administered by an order of nuns but this would in no way influence the non-sectarian nature of the hospital.

The search for a medical director intensified after the Board of Governors established the criteria for his selection and named the search committee. Ed Barry considered this as one of the major challenges in his work with the hospital. He recalls, "Here we were. Here's a new hospital. It's going to succeed only to the extent that we can get the proper caliber of men involved in it. To me, it was a challenging situation."

Dr. Donald Pinkel, head of pediatrics at Roswell Park Memorial Institute in Buffalo, New York, had decided in the spring of 1961 that he was ready for something different, a new challenge. During this time he talked with an old friend, Dr. Michael J. Sweeney, who was in the pediatrics department of the University of Tennessee Medical School in Memphis. Dr. Sweeney talked a lot about the new St. Jude Hospital that was under construction in Memphis. The two speculated on how it might be accepted by the medical community in the area.

Dr. Sweeney recounted stories he had heard including one where a physician had asked Danny Thomas point-blank, "What's in it for you?

Why are you doing this?" Dr. Sweeney seemed convinced that the hospital had merit and that Danny was very serious in his desire to help children with catastrophic illnesses. He asked Pinkel if he might be interested in looking into the opening for medical director.

Pinkel's reply to his friend was, "Well, I can look at it." A few weeks later he met with Dr. James N. Etteldorff, Professor of Pediatrics at the University of Tennessee and Dr. James J. Hughes, Professor and Chief of the Pediatrics division of the University of Tennessee Medical School. Dr. Hughes also sat on the Medical Advisory Committee of St. Jude Hospital. They discussed the director's position and Pinkel promised Dr. Hughes that he would make a trip to Memphis to look into the situation.

He visited Memphis over the Memorial Day weekend and met with Dr. Hughes, Dr. Diggs, Ed Barry and Fred P. Gattas. They took him to see the hospital building which was under construction. And, he was introduced to several members of the medical community and to other Memphis citizens who were involved with the hospital at a dinner at the University Club.

Don Pinkel liked what he saw and heard in Memphis but he was also considering a position at the University of Colorado in Denver. He flew from Memphis to Denver to meet with its representatives. From there he returned home to Buffalo.

He and his wife held serious and lengthy discussions about the two positions. There were so many things to consider — one of the most important their seven children — and they wanted to make the best decision possible for the family.

While Pinkel was considering the two offers, Ed Barry telephoned him and asked if they could meet in Chicago. They agreed on a date and, since Mike Tamer was also to be in Chicago that day, they both met with Dr. Pinkel. The three sat and talked all day.

Dr. Pinkel could see that Barry and Tamer were well versed in the basics of what they wanted in this new hospital. They wanted free medical care for the children who were to be treated and they wanted research that was leukemia and childhood cancer oriented. They had no specifics. They were looking for guidance in the medical area.

That day he sized up Ed Barry as a "real fine man . . . honest, reliable, responsible,

humanistic, highly competent". Tamer he also saw as a "warm humanistic individual — although quite practical, he was also idealistic". He recalls, "We had a good feeling about one another. We were on the same wave length concerning our values."

The fact that all three men, with varied backgrounds but all "on the right track" as far as basic values and priorities were concerned, would be working together convinced Don Pinkel that he should undertake the responsibility of establishing the medical direction of St. Jude Hospital.

In July he met with the Board of Governors and was formally offered the position as first Medical Director of St. Jude Children's Research Hospital. During the summer months he would work on arrangements for operations with the Sisters of St. Francis, on personnel recruitment and on grant applications.

Above: Dr. Donald Pinkel, St. Jude Hospital's first Medical Director.

Don Pinkel, his wife and seven children travelled from Buffalo, New York in late October, arriving in Memphis on the Feast of St. Jude day.

Some might have called that coincidence.

Danny would have said that it was the hand of St. Jude.

"He was one of the most dedicated men I've known in my life. He built this place. All he had was raw materials and he built St. Jude Hospital into a working, beautiful place of excellence."

And Drs. Diggs, Levy and Basile were all pleased with his qualifications. Dr. Pinkel had received his medical degree from the University of Buffalo School of Medicine. He held a research fellowship in childhood cancer at Boston's Children's Hospital Medical Center in 1955 and

Below: The first Board of Governors of St. Jude Children's Research Hospital sits for its first formal portrait in October, 1960.

1956 and then returned to Buffalo to establish a department of pediatrics at Roswell Park Memorial Institute, an internationally known cancer research center. Pinkel was noted for his work with chemotherapy in the treatment of childhood cancer. St. Jude Hospital was to have as its director a man experienced in cancer research *and* in the treatment of children with cancer.

Above: Meetings of the new Board of Governors were working sessions with the usual large amounts of paper work and quite a few discussions with intense differences expressed.

Below: The newest of Memphis' hospitals takes shape in the shadows of St. Joseph Hospital, Memphis' oldest.

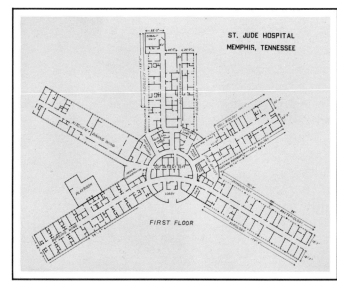

ST. JUDE HOSPITAL
MEMPHIS, TENNESSEE

FIRST FLOOR

Danny's dream takes concrete shape and form. Far left: Dr. Charles E. Malik and friend check progress. Dr. Malik, past president of the General Assembly of the United Nations, had just been named Honorary National President of ALSAC. Left: Ed Barry, Mike Tamer and Fred P. Gattas, check interior progress. Center: Construction underway. Bottom left: The shelled-in building that greeted Dr. Pinkel on his arrival. Bottom right: Floor plan that Dr. Pinkel and Sister Henrita (right) worked with to get the most functional use of the space as possible.

When the new medical director reported for duty on November 1, 1961 he found a building that architects refer to as "shelled in". It had a foundation, exterior and supporting walls, and a roof. Inside was open space, with one exception.

In the wing where his office was to be located he found one room that was "finished". There, with a table and chair plus two wires from outside utility poles — one for telephone and one for light and heater — he set about putting the finishing touches on St. Jude Children's Research Hospital.

The building had been designed in the shape of a five-pointed star with wings radiating from a central hub. This hub was to house the outpatient department, staff offices, record room, blood bank, admitting offices, social services department and a small, non-sectarian chapel.

The second floor of the hub would contain administrative offices, housing for the resident staff and for the Sisters who were to administer the services of the hospital, assembly rooms for meetings, a medical library and schoolrooms for children who were patients.

One wing was to house the in-patient unit with rooms to accommodate thirty-eight children. This wing would also have a playroom for these patients, a television room and small kitchen where mothers could prepare favorite dishes for their children and celebrate special occasions with them.

A second wing would house the kitchen, dining room and related facilities.

A third would contain X-ray and clinical laboratories including chemistry, bacteriology, serology and hematology.

The fourth would be reserved for surgical facilities and central supply units.

The fifth would be used for research and would include offices for the chiefs of the various research services.

Interior plans had been completed for most of the building with the exception of the research wings and the research area of the basement. The balance of the basement area under the central hub section was to be used for shops, laundry, maintenance and a communications center that would include photography and art.

It was felt by all involved in the original planning that the basic scientists who would be using the research area could best design their own working space. Dr. Pinkel was to mention this at the dedication when he said, "I would like to thank Paul Williams for leaving in his design vast amounts of open space so that we could design research facilities as we needed them. He was able to foresee that any great research institution must always be able to re-arrange its facilities to meet the needs of the people it serves."

In arranging the research facilities Don Pinkel made one major change from the original planning. He eliminated completely the planned surgical wing. He made arrangements with St. Joseph Hospital for all surgery to be done there and a tunnel was planned to connect the two hospital buildings. The wing that would have been designated for surgery would be used for research.

The next few months proved to be very hectic. The Board of Governors, with the help of the Medical Advisory Committee, had set up the general framework under which the hospital was to operate. It was Dr. Pinkel's responsibility to translate these generalities into day-to-day activities.

In recruiting a staff his requirements were formidable. A statement made after his appointment gave an indication of what he would be seeking:

"The theme of St. Jude Hospital will be 'Excellence'. We will create an institution whose ideas and functions should be as vital five hundred years from now as they are today. We should build with a long range view — it will take many years to have St. Jude operating at full pace."

"We must find men trained in clinical pediatrics and interested in research and in trying to understand the nature of the serious illnesses of infant and child with the hope of treating them more satisfactorily. We must find laboratory scientists oriented toward these problems in the fields of bio-chemistry, microbiology and others. And we hope to find men of varied backgrounds, interests and personalities who by this very nature will stimulate each other. What St. Jude will be will depend on the people who work in it."

Dr. Pinkel found that recruiting into the Memphis area was not easy. Most clinical and basic scientists that he spoke with were not inclined, on first offering, to make a move to the South. 1961 was still several years away from the beginnings of the great movement toward the Sunbelt.

St. Jude's new Medical Director found that his best move was to keep the person he was recruiting talking on the phone until he had extracted a promise that the person would at least "come down to Memphis and see what we are doing".

This system worked fairly well. But even then it took a great amount of talking and showing once the person arrived in Memphis. One of Dr. Pinkel's first recruits in the basic science area had no idea of moving to Memphis when he ar-

rived to "look it over". But Dr. Allan Granoff liked what he saw and he did move to Memphis. Twenty years later he is still at St. Jude Hospital as Associate Director for Basic Research.

Another doctor made three trips to Memphis before he became convinced that he should accept the position offered him. The first time he spent two or three days talking with those who were already associated with the hospital. It was his first trip to the South, but he was impressed with what was happening at St. Jude. A month later he returned for another three days. Still another month later he was back in Memphis with his wife and family for them to look it over. He spent four months making the decision, but today Dr. H. Omar Hustu, head of Radiotherapy, says that he has never been sorry that he made the move.

While the Medical Director was recruiting his staff, the Sisters of St. Francis were busy staffing the hospital with the personnel needed to maintain housekeeping facilities, storeroom supplies, a dining room and kitchen, and the many areas that were under their supervision. They were also hiring the nurses who would report to Sister Henrita.

Sister M. Henrita had been assigned by the Sisters of St. Francis as the Administrative Director and had been approved by the Board of Governors at their October 1960 meeting. Prior to her assignment at St. Jude she had been Administrator of St. James Hospital in Chicago Heights, Illinois for a period of six years. She was to be in charge of every function of the hospital operation with the exception of Dr. Pinkel's medical and research staffs.

Assisting her was Sister Rita as Business

"The theme of St. Jude Hospital will be 'Excellence.' We will create an institution whose ideas and functions should be as vital five hundred years from now as they are today. We will build with a long range view — it will take many years to have St. Jude operating at full pace."

Left: Two of Dr. Pinkel's early recruits who are still at St. Jude Hospital are at right in top picture, Dr. Allan Granoff, St. Jude's Associate Director of Basic Research and Director of Virology and Dr. H. Omar Hustu, head of Radiotherapy, lower.

Manager. Sister Rita had heard about Danny Thomas and his vow to build St. Jude Hospital and she was delighted when the provincial of her order asked her if she would like to be assigned to Danny's hospital. She joined Sister Henrita in the fall of 1961 and both sisters lived with the sisters at the convent adjacent to St. Joseph Hospital until their living quarters in the hospital building were completed. They had a room in the still-unfinished building from which they worked.

One of their first projects was to establish an operations budget which would be reviewed with Mr. Barry and members of the Executive Committee. A storeroom and receiving room were set up to receive, in a somewhat orderly fashion, everything that was to be ordered from furniture to cleaning supplies. After these preliminaries were completed the ordering began and went on and on and on. But things were meshing well and everything was moving toward the day the hospital would be open and accept its first patients.

Each week there was a meeting of the Executive Committee chaired by Ed Barry. Those who were there at the time are still heard to describe those days as "there was Mr. Barry managing it all". At that time Mr. Barry was not only managing it all — he was paying for a lot of it. Dr. Pinkel recalls when his checks and others were Mr. Barry's personal checks. Mr. Barry also borrowed money from the bank on his signature, as Dr. Pinkel recalls, to meet current expenses on occasion.

Thus, it was no surprise to those involved that the night before the dedication of the hospital there was a banquet honoring Ed Barry. Danny Thomas was the master of ceremonies and the room was filled with Ed Barry's friends . . . his old ones from Memphis and his new ones from all over the country who had gathered in Memphis for the dedication. The ALSAC newspaper in its coverage of the dinner included this statement:

"Edward Francis Barry is the greatest friend St. Jude Children's Research Hospital has! This is an unusual statement but it befits an unusual person. It is no secret that the greatest single factor responsible for bringing to reality this great facility of mercy and hope was Mr. Barry, a prominent Memphis attorney and one of this area's most outstanding civic leaders."

"Besides his tremendous and numerous efforts

on behalf of this project founded by Danny Thomas he personally has contributed over $50,000 of his own funds, making him the largest single individual contributor. Largely because of his efforts the City of Memphis raised nearly $800,000 earlier this year for St. Jude Children's Research Hospital."

An organization that was especially helpful in those hectic days just prior to the opening was the Ladies of St. Jude. This group of dedicated Memphians had organized in 1956 with Mrs. James Dillon as president. In 1961 and 1962 Mrs. John T. Dwyer was president. Mrs. Dwyer's husband was chairman of the building committee of the Memphis Steering Committee. Many of the members of the Ladies of St. Jude were either married to, or related to, the men who served on the various hospital committees. Several were wives of Memphis doctors.

The purpose of the auxiliary was to provide volunteer services to the hospital in any area where they were needed. They would also raise money to fund a playroom for the children and to purchase a station wagon for use by the sisters who were to administer the hospital. Mrs. Frank Tobey, wife of the Mayor, was among the group. Also its first treasurer was Mrs. Nat Buring, whose husband had pledged a substantial amount at the very first fund-raising dinner in Memphis.

Today, Sister Rita pays tribute to this first group of volunteers. "We couldn't have done it as well as we did without the Ladies of St. Jude. These were society women working as if they were being paid by the hour. Their members were told that if they were not going to work 'don't join us'."

Sylvia (Mrs. Nat) Buring, with a great deal of business experience to her credit, volunteered to work in the business office. Sister Rita recalls that she came in only one day a week but on that one day she took complete charge of checking all orders, all invoices and all equipment received. "I don't know how we could have done it without her help," Sister Rita recalls twenty years later.

Top left: Sylvia (Mrs. Nat) Buring at her desk in the business office. Top right: Sister Rita M. Schroeder, Business Manager. Lower: Some of the members of the Ladies of St. Jude, first organized in 1956 and still active today in volunteer work with the hospital.

Helen Hogan joined the Ladies of St. Jude because her mother-in-law was active in the organization and she had suggested that Helen might want to join and do some community service work in her free time. She worked with the pharmacist before the hospital opened, writing letters to pharmaceutical houses asking for donations of drugs to help stock the pharmacy. She helped set up the pharmacy and organize its operation.

But Helen Hogan's story does not end there. After the hospital opened she worked every Thursday in the pharmacy, a total of about thirty volunteer hours a month. George Crevar, the pharmacist, made the mistake of telling Dr. Pinkel how much help she was to him. Dr. Pinkel promptly requisitioned her services and she worked with him, still as a volunteer, for two years.

In 1964 Helen needed a full time job and she transferred to the hospital's payroll working five days a week. In 1965 Dr. Pinkel asked her if she would consider going to work with Dr. Allan Granoff. Since her child was still small she agreed only if she could continue on her nine in the morning until two in the afternoon schedule. This was agreed to, but the work load was so heavy that she started on a full time schedule in the fall of 1965.

Helen is still at St. Jude, still secretary to Dr. Allan Granoff. And, if anyone wants to know anything about the history of the hospital, they are told, "Ask Helen Hogan."

The weather had been wet and sloppy that winter of 1961-1962 but a dedication was planned for February 4, 1962.

The statue of St. Jude Thaddeus that Danny Thomas had ordered from De Prato Statuary in Rome, Italy had arrived and had spent part of the winter lying on its side in its crate in front of the hospital. But the five thousand pound, ten foot tall statue of Bianca-Dura white marble was now in place atop the thousand pound cornerstone that had been waiting to receive it for almost two years. Both the statue and the cornerstone were Danny Thomas' personal gifts to St. Jude Hospital.

In the cornerstone there was a copy of the St. Jude Hospital Foundation of California constitution, a copy of the ALSAC constitution, copies of newspaper articles about the hospital and a half dollar and a quarter.

Preparing for the Grand Opening ceremonies. Left, top: Danny Thomas assures Joe Gattas that "He's just resting" as the statue of St. Jude Thaddeus lies on its side, still crated, waiting to be placed on the cornerstone. Center: Before the crowd arrives a youngster checks to be sure that the statue is in place and (lower) Danny Thomas and Dr. Don Pinkel assure one another that everything is ready and that it will truly be a great day. Above: The shrouded statue awaits the ceremonies. Right: The stage is set and ready for the crowds to gather.

Sunday, February 4, was a bright, sunny day, warm and pleasant, a respite in the cold damp winter. More than nine thousand people from Memphis, from California, from all parts of the country gathered to participate in the dedication ceremony and tour the hospital.

They listened to a story that Danny told them before he unveiled the statue . . . the tale of the fifty-cent piece and the quarter that were sealed in the cornerstone. He had made a fund-raising speech in Peoria, Illinois and a little boy in the audience called out to him. His name was Billy Johnson and he was blind, partially deaf and stricken with cerebral palsy. With great effort, he said, "Hey, Danny Thomas. I want to help the poor sick kids." In his hand was an envelope containing seventy-five cents — the half dollar and the quarter that were in the cornerstone.

Danny told the crowd, "A dream is one thing. A realization is something entirely separate. I should applaud all of you in the sound of my voice, and those who will see pictures of what is happening here. I publicly thank you, wherever you may be, for the support of this dream. It took a rabble-rousing, hook-nosed comedian to get your attention, but it took your hearts, loving minds and generous souls to make it come true. If I were to die this minute, I would know why I was born."

Arnold Graber, a Memphis businessman, remembers the day well. He was in the Christian Brothers High School Band that played at the ceremony. While touring the hospital later he almost ran into Danny Thomas coming around a corner with his usual big cigar in his hand. Dan-ny apologized for the near collision, "Excuse me, son. God bless you."

Graber recalls his answer. It was, "No, sir, God bless you!"

Helen Hogan also remembers the day as exciting. She had arrived about eight o'clock and was to serve as hostess in the pharmacy. At that time guided tours were planned. This was not to be.

Dr. Pinkel also recalls that the minute the dedication was over the crowds moved into the building, unfortunately most through the nearest entrance which was into one of the unfinished research wings!

Helen was still working in the pharmacy at mid-afternoon when Sister Rita asked her if she would relieve on the switchboard. It seemed the regular operator was on the verge of complete collapse. Of course, Helen had never operated a switchboard but since Sister Rita had assured her it was simple and she would show her, she cheerfully complied.

Helen stayed at the switchboard until about 8:30 in the evening when the Board of Governors convened a meeting on the second floor. Sister Rita came and got her and together they headed for the cafeteria and their first meal of the day. For her, it was a most exciting day.

Dr. Pinkel recalls it also as a most beautiful day. "After the Board meeting I walked out after everyone else had gone. I was the last one outside. And, it was the first time the building had been lit up and it was beautiful. I stood out there alone for some time just admiring it."

Formal Opening

OF ST. JUDE RESEARCH HOSPITAL, MEMPHIS, TENNESSEE
2 P. M., SUNDAY, FEBRUARY 4, 1962

Program

Master of Ceremonies .... Edward F. Barry
Presentation of Colors by Naval Air Station Color Guard

The National Anthem .... Mrs. William J. Condon

Invocation .... Right Reverend Monsignor J. Harold
Shea, Dean of West Tennessee

Introduction of Honored Guests

Remarks

Honorable Henry Loeb .... Mayor of Memphis

Rev. James H. Elder .... Pastor, Mullins Methodist Church

Michael F. Tamer .... Executive Director, ALSAC

Honorable Clifford Davis .... United States Representative

Honorable Estes Kefauver .... United States Senator

Honorable Buford Ellington .... Governor, State of Tennessee

Principal Address .... Danny Thomas, Founder, St. Jude
Hospital

Benediction .... Rabbi Sylvin Wolf, Temple Israel

Unveiling of Statue of St. Jude .... Danny Thomas

Tour of Hospital .... Ladies' of St. Jude

Music by Christian Brothers High School Band,
Directed by Ralph Hale

Top right: Ed Barry checks to see that all is in place before beginning the ceremony. Center: Danny is poised for the unveiling of the St. Jude Thaddeus statue and with a tug on the cord it is accomplished. Lower: A cameraman photographing the crowd gets an assist from the Memphis Fire Department, St. Jude supporters from the very beginning.

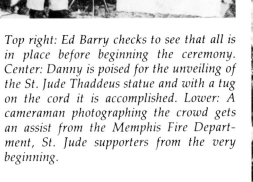

"... the dream of a Catholic; designed by a Methodist-Episcopal Negro architect; built by a firm owned by a Jew; equipped and supported by volunteer Protestants, Roman and Orthodox Catholics, Jews and Moslems; staffed by Anglo-Saxons, Orientals, Negroes and many other ethnic origins — to offer hope to the world's children regardless of race, creed or economic status."

Left: Following the formal dedication, Danny asked the children who had participated with him to join him for a picture. Children from every ethnic and racial group in Memphis were represented. And, as the afternoon shadows lengthen, the shadow of its founder looms large against the cornerstone of St. Jude Children's Research Hospital. Right: The lights were on that night of February 4, 1962 and they have been on every night since while the dedicated staff care for children with catastrophic illnesses day and night.

Danny's hospital was open for business.

St. Jude Children's Research Hospital's first patient was Jonathan Britton. Almost twenty years later, his mother, Mrs. Carol Britton returned to Memphis to visit St. Jude Hospital. During those years every time she heard about the hospital on TV and radio, or read about it in the newspapers, she felt an urge to return to the hospital where her son had died so many years before. It took many years for her to make the visit and to her it was both an emotional and an extremely rewarding experience. She is shown with three young patients.

The First Years

On March 16, 1962 Jonathan Britton was admitted to St. Jude Hospital as its first patient. Jonathan's father was a student at the University of Mississippi and Jonathan had been stricken with leukemia. At the time he was referred to St. Jude less than one percent of children diagnosed with this deadly disease survived.

For three years a group of dedicated researchers, under the direction of Dr. L.W. Diggs, had been conducting research in leukemia and allied blood diseases in children. They had been quartered temporarily in the laboratories of the Hematology department of the University of Tennessee but their research funds had been supplied by ALSAC. The equipment that had been purchased with ALSAC funds was moved into the new research labs at the hospital, a part of the hundreds of thousands of dollars worth of research equipment that would be used to help find the cause and cure for childhood cancers.

Danny's hospital was open for business. It was concrete proof that a part of the medical community in the United States realized the impact that research in the basic sciences was to have on the problems of childhood illnesses. It was an act of faith in the ability of scientists to understand the biology of man from conception to maturity, and its errors, so that prevention of disease in infancy and childhood might one day materialize in their laboratories.

Three of the five wings of the hospital were to be devoted to laboratories for the study of cell biology, bio-chemistry, immunology and micro-biology. One wing was to be used for inpatient treatment while the rotunda would house out-patient services. This provided a maximum opportunity to bring clinical studies to the laboratory and laboratory studies to bear on the children's problems.

From the left: A day at St. Jude could include waiting in the out-patient lobby, below, a game of pool in the playroom, bottom, a visit from Dr. Pinkel and Danny, right, or a quiet moment with a favorite record.

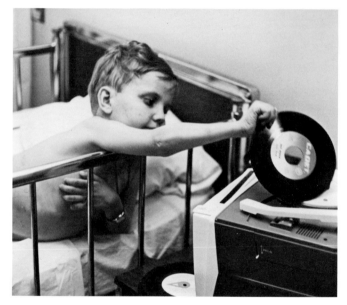

Opposite page: All day long the staff plans for its patients' welfare: a meeting of nurses, clinicians discuss their patients and plan courses of treatment, basic scientists work to discover the cause and cure of the diseases, and (lower right) administration — Dr. Pinkel, Ed Barry and Bernard Palumbo plan additional treatment and laboratory space.

And, since both research and patient care appear to thrive best in a teaching environment, St. Jude was closely associated from the beginning with the University of Tennessee. Members of its scientific staff, including Dr. Pinkel, had been appointed to faculty positions in their respective departments at the university. Even before the hospital opened its doors, ALSAC had created an endowment of $300,000 for a chair at the university for the Director of the hospital.

Arrangements had been made for fellows, residents and graduate students to train at the hospital. Both the hospital and the university administrators knew that only the continuing influx of bright young men and women would assure the continued vitality of the hospital and its work.

St. Jude Hospital would work in connection and cooperation with, but not under the supervision of, the University of Tennessee. It was to be operated by a full-time paid staff and was not to be dependent in any way on volunteer professional services.

Dr. Pinkel set up a combined staff at the hospital. The clinical staff was composed mostly of pediatricians. This staff was expected to devote its full time to the care of the patients and to clinical and laboratory research. They were not to engage in private practice. Residents in pediatrics and hematology fellows would help with the clinical work.

The basic research staff members were scientists, some with Ph.D.'s and some with M.D.'s. They would have little responsibility for the direct care of the patients. They were to engage themselves in laboratory research only. Dr. Pinkel and the members of the Scientific Advisory Board*, were in complete accord that the hospital would seek out top scientists, give them the materials to work with and they would develop research studies that would help in the hospital's battle to find a cause and a cure for childhood cancers.

*Six doctors, all top men in their fields, were invited by the Board of Governors prior to the opening of the hospital to serve as a Scientific Advisory Board. Each member was to serve a three year term, and following the first appointments, the Board was to be self-perpetuating, electing its own members. Members of the original board were: James Arey, M.D., Professor of Pathology at Temple University; Donal Dunphy,

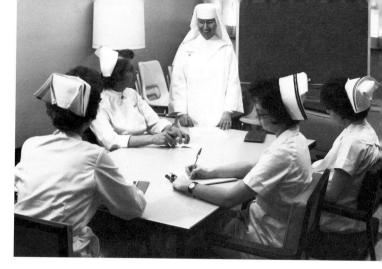

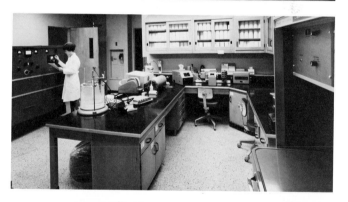

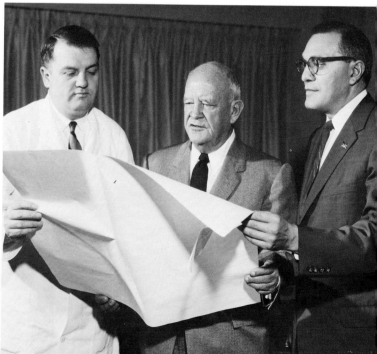

M.D., Professor and Chairman of the Department of Pediatrics at Iowa State University; Morton Levin, M.D., D.P.H., American Cancer Society Career Professor of Epidemiology at Roswell Park Memorial Institute; Erwin Neter, M.D., Associate Professor of Bacteriology at the University of Buffalo; Sydney Rittenberg, Ph.D., Professor of Bacteriology at the University of Southern California; and Phillip Sturgeon, M.D., Director of American Red Cross National Blood Research Center in Los Angeles. (See Appendix for current Scientific Advisory Board.)

This did not mean that there would be two separate institutions under one roof. It did mean that the basic scientists would be free to follow research that they felt important as long as it was related to catastrophic disease. It meant that the clinical staff would treat the patients on a day to day basis and at the same time would gather data for studies that would be used to develop new treatments and protocols. The clinical staff and the basic research staff were expected to work together and they were also expected to work with the staffs of other research institutions.

Some of Dr. Pinkel's ideas were considered quite revolutionary in the medical community at that time. His basic philosophy was to be innovative, to throw away the book and start from "square one". He felt that he and his staff should do what was most reasonable and what was most likely to be fruitful. Everyone associated with the hospital — staff personnel and members of the Board of Governors — were caught up in this idea of "doing something a little different".

In the very first days of planning the book was also thrown away in the area of racial segregation. When Danny Thomas and Cardinal Stritch first talked about the hospital, the Cardinal was adamant that it should be completely integrated. Danny had no problem with this. The members of the St. Jude Hospital Foundation of California had no problem with it. The architect had no problem with it. All were, after all, Californians and there was no segregation policy in their state.

But some of the people in Memphis and the Mid-South area were concerned with the idea. Arnold Shappley recalls that, when he first saw plans that did not call for separate bathroom facilities, he mentioned it to Claude Coyne from the Los Angeles firm. After all, he was supposed to provide input on local regulations and customs. This was, no doubt, an oversight.

Trying to tactfully point out that "it just isn't done in this area" he shook his head in amazement when Coyne's answer was that they were aware of the fact, but, nevertheless, that was the way it was to be. It was not an oversight, as he had thought, but deliberately planned.

During the construction phase of the hospital the Board of Governors did review the statement of policy with regard to segregation. It was decided to continue along the path as planned. No one made a more impassioned plea than Dr. L.W. Diggs, a member of the Board of Governors and a long-time Memphis resident. In a letter to Mike Tamer, he wrote:

"In my opinion, the St. Jude Hospital should be supported by people of all races and we should never allow the segregation problem to interfere with our more important aims."

"Today, a son of one of the technicians in my laboratory died of leukemia after an illness which financially wrecked their family, as well as causing mental and physical strain on members of the family. The hospital bills for this child exceeded $20,000."

"It is for such a disease that St. Jude Hospital is being built. The petty matters of race pale into unimportance in the face of catastrophies of this type."

After the hospital opened, the community became aware of the policy. All other medical facilities in and around Memphis were strictly segregated. There was an undercurrent of concern on the part of the citizenry.

St. Jude was the first hospital in the area to have black and white patients treated in the same room, black and white parents together, as well as integrated dining and bathroom facilities. Dr. John Smith, the first black doctor to serve on the clinical staff of what could be described, in the south, as a white hospital, treated white children. This was quite radical in the early 1960's.

In most Southern white hospitals, black personnel — even those with university degrees —

"St. Jude is an institute of research and I predict that one day it will be one of the most important institutes of research in the world."

were normally employed in service areas. At St. Jude they were moved into the laboratory as technicians and into the clinical area as nurses. They were given positions of responsibility that their training had prepared them for. It never occurred to anyone in the hospital to do otherwise.

There was another problem with the local segregation customs. Many children were to arrive in Memphis from across the country to be treated at the hospital. They were to be referred by their own doctors to St. Jude, and upon acceptance, would travel to Memphis by plane, train, bus or private automobile. If the child were admitted as an in-patient, the accompanying parent would need lodging accommodations. If the child were accepted as an out-patient, both the parent and child would need a place to stay, sometimes for weeks at a time.

It was first planned that the hospital would build and operate a motel facility across the street from the hospital. As time went by and plans for the hospital became firm, this seemed unnecessary. There were hotels in the immediate downtown area, and the Board of Governors felt that the hospital should not go into competition with existing lodging facilities.

Arrangements were made for what was called domiciliary care in a downtown hotel. If the parents were unable to pay for transportation and lodging, the hospital would pick up the tab for all, including meals. The first hotel to be used for domiciliary care was the Claridge. It was a fine hotel and was the closest to the hospital.

But the first attempt to register black children and their parents at the Claridge caused a furor. The hotel was strictly segregated, as were all others in the area. The management advised that they would be happy to provide rooms for white families who came to the hospital but not for black families.

Donald Pinkel issued an ultimatum. If the black children and their parents were not allowed to stay in the hotel, the hotel would not be used for any patients. The hotel management reluctantly agreed, provided the black families would eat in their rooms and not try to enter the downstairs dining room. Again, the hospital administration remained firm. They won, and the Claridge Hotel was to be a primary residence for patients until it closed in December of 1968, a victim of the migration of business from Memphis' downtown area following the assassination

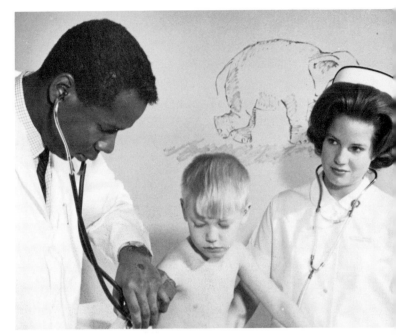

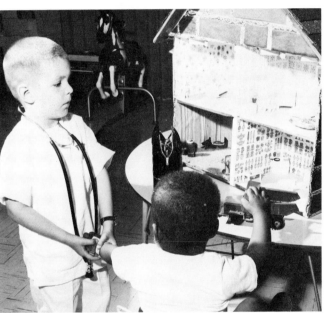

Above: There was never a problem with integration at St. Jude Hospital in those early days as there was in so many places, whether it was playing doctor or a real doctor-patient relationship.

"In a creative environment you have to avoid apathy and complacency. You have to prove yourself every day. You cannot rest on yesterday's laurels."

of Dr. Martin Luther King, Jr. in Memphis in the spring of 1968.

Even though some of the residents and businessmen in Memphis had problems with integration at St. Jude, the staff, the volunteers, the parents and patients did not. Sister Rita recalls, "Our first Christmas party was black and white together — something very unusual in those days — but we didn't make any distinction — we were just one big happy family — everyone belonged!"

There were many hectic times that first year. Two wings were being completed and equipped for basic research. Dr. Pinkel and Ed Brown found that equipping a research hospital was not only an expensive project but a logistical one as well. There were no equipment supply houses in the Memphis area, and all items had to be purchased elsewhere and shipped in, frequently causing delays and frustrations.

A construction problem also arose that year. An application had been made to the National Institutes of Health for matching funds to complete one of the wings. Researchers had been hired and were to report for work in July. But, a construction strike, a not unusual occurrence in Memphis at that time, was called. This problem was solved by the hospital administration in its own innovative way by having the construction workers, who wanted to work, transferred to the hospital payroll for the duration of the strike.

Even more serious was the availability of blood and the demands of the hospital for a constant supply. When Dr. Pinkel arrived in Memphis, he found that all the blood banks in the area were commercial ones that had arrangements with the hospitals to sell them blood as needed.

The blood banks would pay the donor five dollars, sell to a hospital for twenty-five dollars, and the hospital would bill the patient thirty-five dollars. This was to present a problem at St. Jude since it was planned that no patient would ever receive a bill for services — including blood. And paying the commercial blood bank charges seemed quite unreasonable.

The same innovative thinking used to solve other problems was applied here and an appeal for blood donors went forth into the community. St. Jude would have and maintain its own volunteer blood bank.

Many responded, among them the officers and men at the Naval Air Station just north of Memphis, the same base whose men had presented Danny Thomas with a check for the hospital in 1955. Commanders of the naval and Marine units would allow their men who volunteered to be bussed into the hospital on Sunday mornings to donate blood. Another bus would go in on Wednesdays, and any off-duty personnel could go then and donate blood. The men received no payment from the hospital or the Navy but they did receive weekend passes for each donation. Liberty in downtown Memphis was an added pleasure to the joy of helping the children at the hospital.

Prisoners at the Penal Farm to the east of the city who volunteered were bussed to the hospital on Saturdays to donate blood. Their reward — steak for dinner.

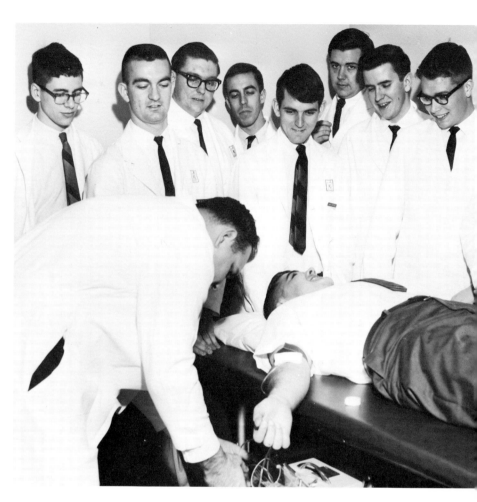

Right: Even the residents who were training at St. Jude Hospital were enthusiastic about the Blood Bank. Here, a group lends moral support to a fellow student about to donate his share.

Students from colleges in the area, members of clubs and fraternal organizations and private citizens all became involved with the hospital during this campaign. Many later became active with ALSAC in fund-raising because of their introduction to the hospital via the blood donor program.

Eventually a community blood bank was started in Memphis, from which the hospital could draw a blood supply, but not until after St. Jude had solved its own problem in its own way — innovation at work!

One major hurdle was also cleared in July of 1962. As Dr. Pinkel relates, the hospital had been hiring a staff, accepting patients and "praying for Mr. Barry's continued good health". Mr. Barry was still assuming the responsibility for a great deal of the hospital construction expense. In July ALSAC voted to assume the balance of the construction costs of over a million dollars and repaid Ed Barry for the money he had advanced, with the exception of the very sizeable donation he had made to the hospital.

Dr. Pinkel asserts, "The rock of Gibraltar was Ed Barry. Without him, it wouldn't have gotten off the ground." Ed Barry, unassumingly, recalls his role in the beginning years of St. Jude in a somewhat different fashion.

"I don't think it happened the way Danny says it did . . . I don't believe I played anything like the prominent part he often alludes to. I just happened to occupy certain positions and was in certain spots where I could be helpful."

Ed Barry is still Chairman of the Board of Governors at St. Jude Hospital. In his message that appeared in the 1980 scientific annual report of the hospital, twenty-five years after he first met Danny Thomas, he wrote:

"Maintaining a research center that does not charge for its services is a perfect example of the love and concern felt by supporters of St. Jude Children's Research Hospital. In the final analysis, that is the main reason all of us — staff, scientists, board and ALSAC — are here . . . love, and the sharing of a dream, and for our efforts we've been rewarded a thousand times over."

That was all the recognition necessary for Ed Barry, the man "who brought the hospital to Memphis".

The Medical Library, supported by members of the Salon Circle of Memphis, contained over 250 volumes and subscriptions to 80 journals that first year. Volunteer members of the Ladies of St. Jude help to keep it in order.

That first year, 126 patients were admitted to St. Jude Hospital. These children verified that the hospital was operating under the ground rules that it had set up for itself. The group included children of all ages with a variety of catastrophic diseases including neuroblastoma, lymphosarcoma, Wilms tumor, glioma, osteosarcoma and leukemia. The majority were leukemia patients and they were male and female; black and white; Catholic, Protestant and Jew ... as Danny Thomas had vowed. And not one was charged for any service rendered.

The staff by the end of the year numbered 108, and they were very excited by that first year's studies. As they admitted more patients, originated more studies and evaluated the results as they came in, they saw that these results looked very promising in many areas. They became even more enthusiastic. More than thirty research projects had been instituted, four had been completed and others were continuing. And, during that very busy year staff members had also found time to publish more that a dozen papers in professional journals.

The medical library, at the end of that first year, included 253 books and subscriptions to 80 journals. This library was supported by the Salon Circle of Memphis. In 1955, just after the announcement was made that St. Jude would be built in Memphis, Mrs. Mark Cowles, the president of the Salon Circle, began a series of calls at-

tempting to reach one of the members of the Memphis Steering Committee.

The Salon Circle, one of the oldest women's organizations in Memphis, was looking for a philanthropic project. Organized in the late 1800's as a select group of Jewish women who were associated with the arts ... poets, authoresses, musicians and visual artists ... the Circle grew into a cultural group with its main interest the furthering of fine arts in Memphis.

While reading about the hospital, the members had decided that they would like to sponsor a music room, at the hospital. But Mrs. Cowles was having difficulty reaching Barry, Canale or Gattas ... they had been deluged with calls about the hospital and were having a hard time just keeping up with events as they happened. Mrs. Cowles was well aware of the problem and she kept trying. Then fate, or St. Jude, entered the picture. One day while she was working in her family's business office, across the street from the National Bank of Commerce, she saw Danny Thomas leave a bright red convertible and enter the bank building. Not one to miss such a golden opportunity, she hastily wrote him a note, telling him of the Salon Circle and its interest in a project with the hospital. She walked across the street and tucked the note into the steering wheel of the car.

The next day her phone rang with a call to let her know that, indeed, the hospital would be most interested in the ladies of the Salon Circle sponsoring a project.

After much discussion, the ladies became aware that the music room they had visualized was not appropriate for the new hospital. It was suggested that they might wish to sponsor the medical library. An agreement was reached and the Salon Circle members started holding fund-raising events for their project.

Over the years, the Salon Circle has donated more than $40,000 to the hospital for the library. It has also furnished the portraits of Danny Thomas and Dr. Pinkel that hang on either side of the stage in the auditorium in the new tower.

Once a year the Circle, about a hundred and fifty member group now, holds a luncheon meeting after which its members adjourn to St. Jude Hospital to visit "their" library and present a yearly check for additional volumes for its shelves.

The next two years saw the completion of the last wing that included a cobalt therapy unit. The first x-ray therapy units were installed in 1964. No longer was it necessary for a doctor or a technician to wheel a patient through the tunnel to St. Joseph Hospital and wait until the X-ray was available.

These two years also began a "moving around" pattern that was to continue to the present time. There was always the search for room to add new areas for research or clinical care, for better utilization of the space provided within the five wings of the Star of Hope.

In 1963 and 1964, another 300 patients were added to the patient roster and the staff increased to 183. The same two years saw the operational budget for the hospital top the million dollar a year figure.

In less than three years, St. Jude Children's Research Hospital was responding to the needs of patients from half the states in the United States, including far-away Alaska.

The years 1965 and 1966 were a time for re-appraisal and re-organization at St. Jude. In 1965 the Scientific Advisory Board recommended that a single person should be responsible for the entire operation of the hospital. The members felt that there should be no division of responsibility.

The Board of Governors accepted the recommendation and the administrative responsibility was transferred from the Sisters of St. Francis to Dr. Pinkel in addition to his medical and scientific supervision.

The Sisters of St. Francis would relinquish their day-to-day administration, but they were to continue to serve the hospital in its relationship with St. Joseph's, as members of the Board of Governors, and would be appointed to serve on committees as they were appointed throughout the years.

Among those that were involved through the years were Sister Luciano, who had set up the nursing program when the hospital opened. She was to remain as head of the nursing staff until 1972. Sister Rita, who returned to Memphis in the late 1960's as Administrator of St. Joseph Hospital, was appointed to serve on the Clinical Trials Committee, a group of scientific advisors that assures that the rights of the patients are protected at all times and that all protocols for any treatment are first studied by this committee. And Sister Mary Ann Guthrie, of the Dominican order, was to join the staff in the late 60's to work with its nutritional program.

Staff members continued to be attracted to the hospital from all parts of the United States as well as from European, South American and Asian countries. The end of 1966 found St. Jude with a staff of 191, 325 new patients and a budget for yearly operational expenses at just over a million and a half dollars.

November of 1966 was also a milestone in the treatment of leukemia at St. Jude Hospital. It marked the first time that any leukemia patient had ever been taken off treatment. Dr. Pinkel and his fellow clinicians were convinced that prolonged treatment was not good for the children, that they should have what was needed and no more. But, what was needed?

That November, Dr. Pinkel talked with parents of five children who were being treated for acute lymphocytic leukemia. All five were in remission, the medical term that signifies the complete absence of apparent cancer cells. Dr. Pinkel proposed to take them off all treatment. They would continue to come to the hospital for regular check-ups and clinical study. All the parents accepted his suggestion.

All five children who were taken off therapy that November of 1966 are still in remission today. All five are now adults, and some have children of their own.

In retrospect, Dr. Pinkel's observation is, "It

1966 was a landmark year for St. Jude Hospital. In November, Dr. Pinkel took five children off all treatment for leukemia — all five are still in remission today! Also that year Memphis honored Danny Thomas by naming the street that bordered the hospital for him (below) and in October Danny Thomas and Ed Barry burned the mortgage for the construction of the hospital (right)!

seemed to be the right thing to do. I just took the bull by the horns."

Of the patients who were admitted to St. Jude with acute lymphocytic leukemia from 1962 through 1967, seventeen percent survived. The patients comprising that seventeen percent are still alive today.

The goal then became to increase the percentage of survival from this dreaded disease until there would be no fatalities. At the same time, the basic researchers would continue to search for the cause and a cure for the disease.

The fall of 1966 was also another memorable milestone in the history of St. Jude Hospital. Danny Thomas and Ed Barry burned the mortgage for the construction of the building!

Entering 1968, excitement was at an all-time high at St. Jude Hospital. It was the beginning of maelstrom years, mildly chaotic, which Dr. Pinkel welcomed. He believed that a creative environment thrives on just such an atmosphere.

St. Jude was accepting more referrals of children with leukemia than any other institution in the United States. The number of patients under study was more than a thousand and the staff felt that its research was headed for a point where they might be able to think in terms of a cure for leukemia. Being cautious, as all research scientists are, they were not speaking out in public about it, but they, themselves, felt that it was possible to hope for a cure for the dreaded childhood disease.

But, while the staff was optimistic about the hospital's leukemia studies, they, and the citizens of Memphis, were dramatically faced with another problem.

In April of 1968, Dr. Martin Luther King, Jr. was killed in a motel in downtown Memphis, not far from the hospital itself. The citizens of Memphis were in no way responsible for the action of the killer, who was not even a resident of the city. And certainly, the doctors and staff at St. Jude, many of whom came from the far corners of the world, were not responsible.

The residents of the two communities of Memphis, black and white, were concerned. They felt that their community, already split from the strikes and marches that had been held, was in danger of collapse. Citizens of both races worked at establishing lines of communication to narrow the rift.

Members of the St. Jude staff were also concerned about their adopted home. Several banded together to see where they might be able to help. They decided to set up a clinic for children from the poorer communities — to be open in the evenings and on their own time. Somehow they all seemed to feel that one of the frustrations and problems of the poor was health care. This was one area where they felt their services would make a difference.

Dr. Pinkel was joined by other doctors — Simone and Walters from hematology, Smith from virology, Borello from immunology and hematology, and Zee from nutrition and metabolism. The wives of Dr. Simone and Dr. Borello joined the group, as did Mary Nell Adair, a dietician; Loretta Shores, a social worker; and Mary Beth Hudson, a dietician.

After the clinic was established, one fact surfaced that they had not anticipated. They found that there was much more malnutrition in the community than they had believed possible. When they began to talk about this discovery, they were met with denials from some of the people of Memphis, including some local officials.

"There was no such thing as malnutrition in a country like the United States; and certainly none in Memphis, Tennessee." But the group's studies showed conclusively that it was there — more perhaps the result of lack of knowledge about nutrition rather than the absolute lack of food.

Left: St. Jude staff ran a volunteer clinic in 1968 in one of the poorest communities in Memphis. Here, a doctor goes into a home to examine the children.

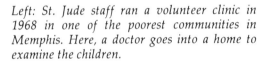

"Adequate diet is more important than compulsory education. If the brain cells don't develop in the first six months of life they never will. And without enough brain cells you can't learn."

Below: Two of the youngsters who participated in the nutrition clinic. Terry, left, looks like a normal child of three or four years. But Terry is eight years old, as is her friend, Marie.

With the help of many concerned citizens, the St. Jude team instituted a program in cooperation with a group called MAP-South (Memphis Area Project South). MAP-South was organized in 1964 when the people of South Memphis formed a community organization to explore means of breaking the poverty cycle in their neighborhood. By 1968, it was fairly well established in the community and was receiving federal assistance from the U.S. Office of Economic Opportunity.

The St. Jude program was an all-volunteer effort. Medical students donated their time to go into the community and work. Food supplies were solicited throughout the area and distributed through MAP-South. But they could see that more was needed.

Dr. Paul Zee had graduated from the University of Amsterdam in 1954 with an M.D. degree, trained in pediatrics. He came to the United States where he received his Ph.D. in nutritional bio-chemistry from Tulane University. He joined the staff at St. Jude in 1963 as chief of nutrition and had been working on nutritional problems in the laboratories of the hospital since 1964. But Dr. King's death acted as a catalyst and moved his program ahead at a greatly accelerated pace.

Dr. Zee was familiar with hunger. He had had personal experience as a child of twelve during the Second World War just before the Allied breakthrough at the Ardennes. His father was a physician and they were, by local standards, well off financially. But they did not have food. No one did. He recalls, "All we could think of was food, how to steal or beg something to eat."

Dr. Pinkel convinced the Board of Governors that malnutrition was, indeed, a catastrophic disease in the United States. The study of it was made a part of the program at the hospital. The St. Jude studies showed that a child's growth pattern was established in the first six months of its life. An infant formula was developed that was provided, by the City of Memphis, at no charge to the parents for the first six months for any infant that had been born at the City of Memphis Hospital.

A supplemental food program was set up by MAP-South and families who were enrolled in the program could go to a warehouse in the community and receive nutritional food for their children. Another program was set up to provide nutritional food for expectant mothers.

All children who were involved in the program from the MAP-South area participated in studies set up by the research teams at St. Jude. These children came from an area that included nine census tracts with ten thousand families, two-thirds of them with income levels below $2,600 a year.

The program sparked a great deal of interest among the St. Jude community, itself, including the Board of Governors. Emily Hajar, sister of Emile Hajar, member of the board and one of the first of the Arabic-speaking "brothers" of Danny Thomas to become involved with St. Jude Hospital, left her home and job in Massachusetts to spend a year in Memphis working as an unpaid volunteer with the nutrition program.

A local Memphis television station also became interested and made a documentary about the food program, but they could find no commercial sponsors for it in the Memphis business community. They put it into syndication and Senator Hubert Humphrey saw it broadcast in Minnesota. He became very interested in the concept, and, with St. Jude scientists furnishing the data that he needed from their studies, he introduced legislation that would change the Child Nutrition Act. This eventually led to the WIC (Women, Infant and Children) program that feeds those who need it across the nation.

Through a strong desire to help all they could, a small band of St. Jude personnel had been responsible for the institution of a program that would be a continuing study in malnutrition. To the St. Jude researchers, malnutrition was "unconstitutional". It was also "unethical and immoral". As such, it was not to be tolerated.

The last day of 1969, the end of a decade in history, brought the culmination of a great effort at St. Jude. The years 1968 and 1969 had added 973 patients to the 926 of the previous years, 1962 through 1967. It saw the staff increase by a total of 253. And, the operating expenses of the hospital had increased to over three million dollars a year!

But all the accomplishments of that decade culminated in a statement published by St. Jude's Medical Director, Dr. Donald Pinkel, in May of the following year, 1970:

"Leukemia can no longer be considered an incurable disease."

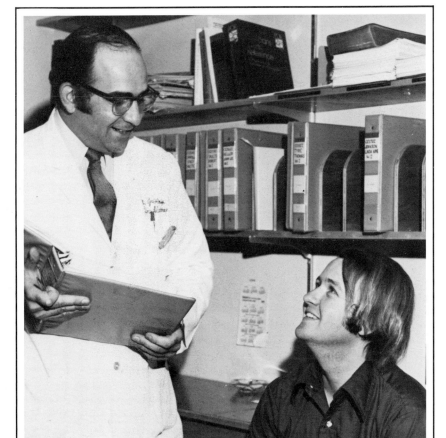

Left: Dr. Joseph Simone discusses his medical record with Pat Patchell. Pat was admitted to St. Jude in January of 1964 with leukemia. He was one of five patients taken off all medication by Dr. Pinkel in November of 1966. He returns to the hospital for regular check-ups and to be a part of the continuing study that may help unlock the key to the cause and cure of childhood cancer.

"Two biggest achievements in terms of child health practice at St. Jude have been the demonstration that acute leukemia cannot be considered incurable and that cure is possible; and the MAP-South program contribution that was highly significant and of international importance. That changed attitudes all over the United States. The general opinion now is that health care givers must accept the responsibility — leukemia and malnutrition need not be accepted."

The Star of Hope Rises to New Heights

During its first eight years the character and direction of St. Jude Children's Research Hospital had been firmly established. It was a uniquely different biomedical research institution. The staff had demonstrated its ability to both originate and innovate and had established a firm foundation for its further growth and development.

The successes of the hospital prompted Dr. Pinkel to quote, somewhat ironically, from the then current edition of the Handbook of Pediatrics under the heading "leukemia":

"There is no cure for leukemia; treatment is directed at prolonging life and relieving symptoms."

He followed up that quotation with a statement:

"Now you see why I never use a textbook to guide me. We can expect a five-year cure rate for 50% of our patients. That's not bad for an incurable disease."

In setting up its innovative program for treatment of its young patients, the staff had developed a total care policy that was like no other. All children accepted into the hospital were on a total care basis with all medical needs of the children taken care of including dental and surgical.

The treatment used for children with leukemia involved a combination of chemotherapy, drugs and radiation. The drugs caused the children to lose all immunity while they were under the treatment program, and it was necessary for the doctors at St. Jude to have complete control over the child's medical program to effectively treat his disease.

And, the young patient's treatment was discussed on a continuing basis by a group of staff members from various departments. They discussed the child's disease, determined the method of treatment and supervised its administration. All were responsible for the general well-being of the child.

By 1970 it was obvious to Dr. Pinkel and the Board of Governors of St. Jude Hospital that the original building, not yet ten years old, did not have the space necessary to treat the ever-increasing flow of children who were admitted for treatment and the ever-expanding research efforts conducted by the basic scientists.

The patient roster continued to grow in numbers because once a child was accepted for treatment, and made a part of a study, that child would continue to return to St. Jude for treatment and examination for the rest of his life. Even after the malignancy that the child was treated for was in remission — even lengthy remission periods — the child would continue to be a patient of the hospital and would be a part of the continuing studies conducted by the scientists.

The research programs that were being conducted were ever increasing, and space was badly needed for the personnel who were involved in this research. Even with a constant moving-around process to better utilize the existing space, it was evident that more was needed.

Plans for a 4-million dollar, seven-story tower were announced on October 28, 1971, just three months before St. Jude Hospital was to celebrate its tenth anniversary. A local Memphis architectural firm, Walk Jones & Frances Mah, Inc. was to design the addition that would be used primarily to house research efforts.

The original hospital plans drawn by Paul Williams had been designed to accommodate a second floor above all five wings of the hospital. This would not give the square footage that was needed, however, and the decision was made to reach toward the sky with the new addition.

Dr. Pinkel worked closely with the architects in the design and the plans for construction. His major concern was that the hospital could not lose even a square foot of functional space while the new building was under construction. Plans were made so that no work areas were to be interrupted.

Ground was broken for the new addition on December 18, 1972. Again, it was another beautiful winter day in Memphis, Tennessee. Despite a brisk wind the sun was shining, and Danny Thomas explained it this way, "It's incredible that anytime we plan something for St. Jude here in Memphis, the weather changes for the better."

The way Danny Thomas was wielding the shovel that day caused some in the audience to feel that he planned to dig the foundation right there at that time — and all by himself.

But all was not as sunny as it appeared to be that bright day. The cost estimate for the addition had doubled. The projected four million had become eight million. The federal government had promised five million of the needed funds, however.

Since the beginning of the hospital, grants had been made to its research programs from government and private agencies including: the National Institutes of Health, the National Science Foundation, the National Library of Medicine, the Community Health Service and the American Cancer Society. In 1970 the federal government had instituted a policy that was to reduce sharply the amount of money that the government was to use to fund medical research.

St. Jude Hospital had received through its first ten years government grants that represented from 30 to 45% of its total operating budget. These grants were not made in a haphazard fashion. It took a solid research program to obtain a grant. The doctor, or research group, applying for the grant to be used for a specific

Left: Ed Barry exhorts the shovel wielders at the groundbreaking for the new addition to "dig in." From the left are Mike Tamer, 10-year employees Dr. Thomas Avery and Marguerite Merritt, and Danny Thomas. Right: Danny digs a deep hole but Mike Tamer really appears to be giving the task his all. Below: The spectators applaud their efforts.

81

Above: St. Jude Hospital's friend in Congress, Representative Dan Kuykendall, with Paul Williams, Danny Thomas and Fred P. Gattas. Below: Signing the construction contract for the new seven-story addition are Danny Thomas, Ed Barry and Mike Tamer.

project would first define the area of study and present the request to the medical director.

Once approved by the medical director, the grant application would be written in minute detail and forwarded to the appropriate agency. Grant applications were made not only to the agencies of the federal government, but some were also directed to private foundations and agencies that had funds which were directed to the specific areas of research that the scientists at St. Jude were involved with.

A great amount of time and effort goes into a grant application. On the part of the hospital several persons are involved on almost a full-time basis with grants and grant applications. On the part of the organization that is to make the grant there is also a great deal of study. Most will send a study committee to tour the facility, to talk with the researchers who are making application to assess the direction the research will take, as well as reviewing the grant application.

To help fund the new tower for St. Jude Hospital, application had been made for federal funds in the amount of five million dollars. Approval had been received but, while the tower was under construction, Carl Simmons, who had joined the staff in 1968 as administrator, was informed by the government agency that it had run out of money and none would be forthcoming.

But fate — or, as Danny would say, St. Jude — intervened in behalf of the hospital. About the time that Simmons was being advised of the cut in funds John Ford Canale received a call from Dan Kuykendall, representative in Congress from the district that included the hospital. Canale, a lawyer and member of the St. Jude Hospital Board of Governors, was also very much involved in local politics.

Kuykendall wanted Canale to head a committee in his re-election campaign. Canale agreed but followed his acceptance with, "I want you to do something for me, too." He explained about the funding problem that had arisen. Representative Kuykendall told Canale that he was going to the White House that day to meet with the President.

After that meeting he called Canale with the assurance "You're going to get your money." And, they did.

It reminded the old-timers of Joe Robbie from Minneapolis, Minnesota and a member of the Board of Governors. While the hospital was under construction, a grant application was buried deep within the bureaucracy that is our government. Joe Robbie was quite active in Democratic politics and, at that time, the administration was controlled by the Democrats.

He headed for Washington, with Danny Thomas in tow, direct to the office of the bureaucrat . . . told his story and the grant application was moved from the bottom of the pile to the top with alacrity. The funds that were sorely needed were forthcoming. And they would continue to come through the hospital's first decade.

For this hospital . . . founded in dedication to a vow of an out-of-work comedian; operated with determined daring through its early years by a dedicated director, staff and Board of Governors; funded by an all-volunteer organization composed mostly of second and third generation Syrian/Lebanese Americans . . . had earned the respect of the nation and its leaders and the organizations they headed.

It was, at the end of its first ten years, one of the highest research facilities on the grant list of the National Cancer Institute. And, to re-affirm its position in the federal government's estimation, in the summer of 1971, the United States Senate voted overwhelmingly to authorize forty million dollars for pilot programs in child nutrition. The program was based on the research that had been conducted, and was still on-going, at St. Jude Children's Research Hospital following those dark days of 1968 in Memphis. Leading the fight on the floor of the Senate was Hubert Humphrey, who had first heard about St. Jude's studies through a television documentary and who was to fall victim himself to the disease St. Jude Hospital was dedicated to eliminate, cancer.

In November of 1975, Danny Thomas dedicated the new seven story tower calling the day "the greatest day in my life". The 118,000 square feet of floor space would house an auditorium, meeting rooms and two floors for inpatient care. The remainder would be used for much-needed research space.

In a taped message played at the dedication, President Gerald Ford said that the opening represented "a great day for our nation and for the children of our country stricken with catastrophic diseases". He concluded with the wish that "as you open the doors to your new seven-story addition, all Americans join in the hope that behind these doors will be found

Construction of new tower. Architect's rendering, right; framework is completed, below left; final beam is prepared for topping off ceremony, following steelworker's tradition of carrying the American flag and a Christmas tree to the top with it, below, right; Bottom: Mrs. J. Don Blankenship, president of the Ladies of St. Jude, gives Ed Barry a check from the organization to pay the cost of the final beam while Joe Gattas looks on approvingly.

many of the medical answers you so diligently seek".

But the joy in the expansion of the hospital was not without a certain air of sadness. The two years previous had seen a passing of the old guard at the hospital and in the ALSAC organization.

In 1972 Dr. Donald Pinkel advised the Board of Governors that he felt the time had come, as it does to all organizations, for a change in leadership at St. Jude Hospital. He felt that a research institution, particularly, must have new concepts and new directions in order to fulfill its obliga-

Left: Arriving for the dedication, Rose Marie and Danny Thomas are met by Ed Barry and John Ford Canale with a large group of supporters of St. Jude Hospital. Below: Once again a crowd gathers at the foot of the statue of St. Jude Thaddeus for the dedication ceremony. Lower: The changing of the guard was reflected by the appearance at the ceremonies of both Dr. Mauer (left) and Dr. Pinkel (right).

tion to society. Don Pinkel wanted to return to the laboratory but wanted to remain a part of St. Jude Hospital's research program in a continuing study of solid tumors in children.

A search committee was appointed in June of 1972 by the Board of Governors to find a successor to Dr. Pinkel. It consisted of Ed Barry and four members of the Scientific Advisory Board, with Dr. Aaron Bendich as chairman. At a meeting of the Board of Governors in May 1973, the search committee presented their choice to the Board, Dr. Alvin M. Mauer.

Dr. Mauer was a pediatrician with extensive experience with childhood cancer. He had been director of hematology at Children's Research Foundation in Cincinnati and professor of pediatrics at the University of Cincinnati.

As Dr. Mauer took over the helm of St. Jude Children's Research Hospital, he stressed not only his appreciation of the attitude of St. Jude Hospital but also his desire to maintain it. He remarked, "With the opportunities that our new building presents, there are also the hazards of going from a small organization to a large one. A very important consideration in the next few years is going to be the preservation of the sense of identity that the people here have with the hospital. We must not let it grow into some huge impersonal machine."

85

Michael F. Tamer
1904-1974

And, in November of 1974, the hospital staff and the ALSAC staff mourned the death of Mike Tamer at the age of 70. In December of the year before he had expressed, once again, a need to retire. Many times in the previous years he had talked with Danny Thomas about retiring. But, like Thomas, he could not bring himself to do it.

He felt the weight of the responsibility for the children at St. Jude heavy on his shoulders and he made the pledge, "I will see the new addition completed and paid for before I even consider retiring." He did not make it, but his many friends were to see that his hopes and dreams for the hospital were carried out.

A Corporate Structure Evolves

With the opening of the new research tower, the floor space of St. Jude Hospital more than doubled. It also signaled a move that was inevitable ... from a "family" organization that was very successfully operating an extraordinary hospital to a much more highly structured corporate entity. This brought with it challenges that were eagerly awaited ... but also presented many new ones.

The initial burst of creativity that had put St. Jude Hospital in the forefront of research in childhood catastrophic diseases had passed and the doctors and scientists were settling down to a day-to-day pattern that often caused them to look back at what they called "the good old days" with a certain nostalgic air.

Some of the doctors recall the stimulation when a small group of clinicians and basic researchers would get together over a cup of coffee and discuss their problems. Others remember that the basic scientists and clinicians were forced to work together because of lack of sufficient physical space ... they were literally sitting on one another's laps.

One doctor reflects today, "In many ways progress can be an enemy. The intimacy of St. Jude, the small unit of overcrowded conditions forced people to know each other real well, forced doctors to know scientists, forced families to get to know other families. It was more cramped, more crowded, but it was nice emotionally. With progress, technology and space there goes a lot of meaningful contact."

No one understood this more than Dr. Alvin Mauer. From the beginning of the hospital, a balance had always been maintained between the clinical and basic sciences. Dr. Mauer was determined that no matter how large the hospital grew in square footage or number of staff personnel, both the balance and the personal contact of the two divisions would continue."

"Many of us yearn for the good old days when we were a part of a small family at the hospital. But I still get a feeling that I'm doing something great. I loved it then . . . I love it now . . . who's to say what period of time was the greatest? I still get a thrill when I come across Danny Thomas Boulevard and see the sign that says St. Jude Children's Research Hospital."

Today he recalls that period and talks about where the hospital is now: "We are coming closer together. We are sharing information. We are perceiving each other's problems and opportunities. It is a goal I have that we may never fully accomplish to my entire satisfaction but we must continue to work on it. We must continue to have an environment where the basic scientists and the clinical investigator are always talking and exchanging information."

He continues, "We cannot expect a basic scientist to work on clinical problems nor can we expect a clinician to know all the ins and outs of laboratory research. What we have been trying to do is build a bridge of people who are involved in clinical problems but who are also skilled laboratory scientists. We've come a long way but we have not accomplished it fully yet. We will continue to work on it."

Another major step for the staff was the change of emphasis of the hospital to life and living and away from death and dying. In 1962, the first patients who were admitted to the hospital were expected to die. A part of the treatment was to help ease the pain of doing so, both physically and emotionally.

The staff could not promise that the child would live . . . it could only hold out "hope" and the assurance that St. Jude Hospital was staffed with doctors and scientists who were devoting all their time to seeking a way to make that "hope" a reality.

From the beginning, the doctors worked to build trust. Because the smaller children could

_____

"We cannot foresee what benediction words of hope may bestow. I have told the story elsewhere of one who asked his doctor what boon he supposed to be the most desired of him by his patients. Was it diagnosis, or medicines, or skill or kindly counsel? No! None of these are the most precious. What the patient yearned for, the remedy to put the most heart into him, was HOPE."

— *Sir Clifford Allbutt ("Lancet" 1922)*

_____

Above: From the beginning Dr. Pinkel talked honestly with both the parents and the child. Strong emphasis was placed on total family involvement.

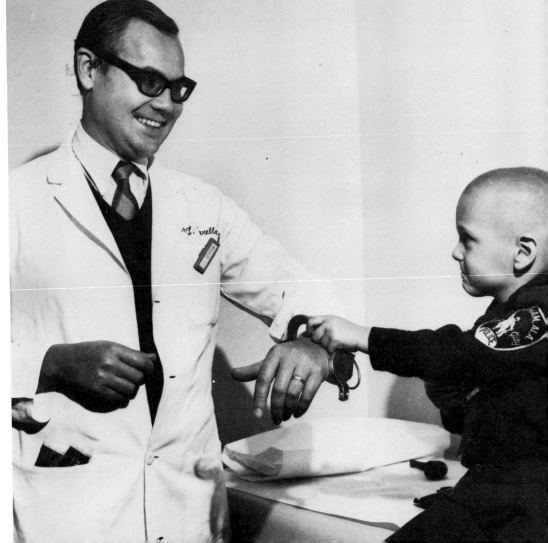

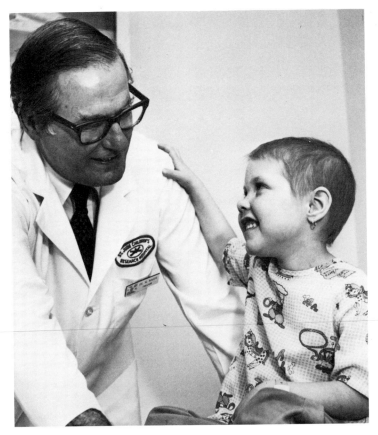

90

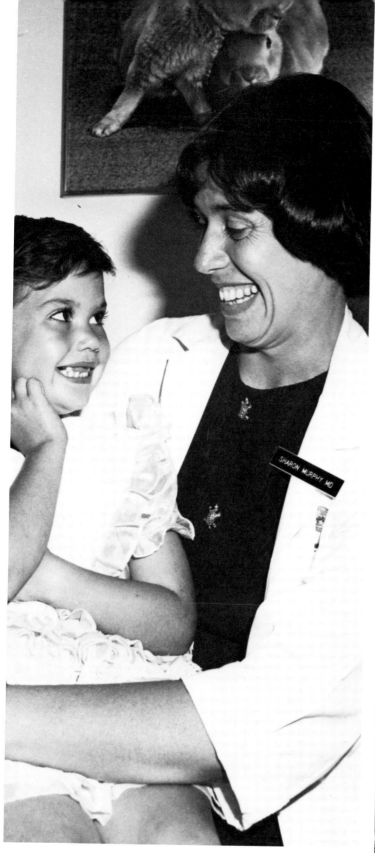

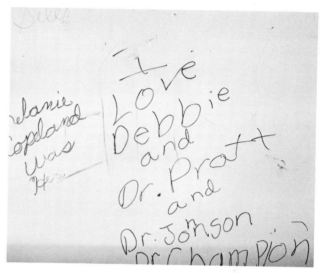

Doctors and their patients develop close relationships as shown by snap shots and messages they receive.

not rationalize, they had to be given a feeling of trust. One method of building this was that each child was cared for by the same doctor each time the child came to the hospital for treatment.

An explanation of the illness and the treatment that would be necessary was given in as much detail as the child's age would allow. Strong emphasis was placed on family involvement. It was important to maintain a relationship that was as normal as possible, especially in an environment that could be very frightening to a child.

From the earliest days of the hospital, Dr. Pinkel insisted on complete honesty in relationships between patient, family and the staff. At that time it was often believed that it was best not to tell the patient the truth about his illness. Dr. Pinkel believed that families are strong . . . that they can handle unbelievable stress if they know in advance what is going to happen. With this approach and concentrating on each child and that child's illness . . . not on "children with catastrophic illness" as a group . . . the doctors and staff treated the patients.

With the success of the treatments that evolved from the studies made at St. Jude, it became apparent to the clinicians and researchers that these children now had a chance. They had successfully leaped the first hurdle — the one that saw children dying and the absolute need to do something about it.

They had seen the ray of light at the end of the tunnel and they became almost Messiah-like in their determination. The totality of the hospital was to keep children alive and healthy.

This, then, presented a new problem — how to help the children who were to live, some for a few years and others for what would be called a "normal" lifetime; how to help them adjust to the psychological problems of living with a chronic illness; and how to help not only the patient but the parents, siblings, relatives and peers.

In June of 1973, the first federal grant was made to the psychiatric program of St. Jude Hospital for $34,000. Grants at that time were relatively non-existant for the study of the adjustment of a child to living with a chronic illness, to the adjustment of the family in relation to the child's illness, or to the adjustment of a child with his peers both in and out of school. Studies were also needed on the effect of radiation and the treatment that sometimes went on

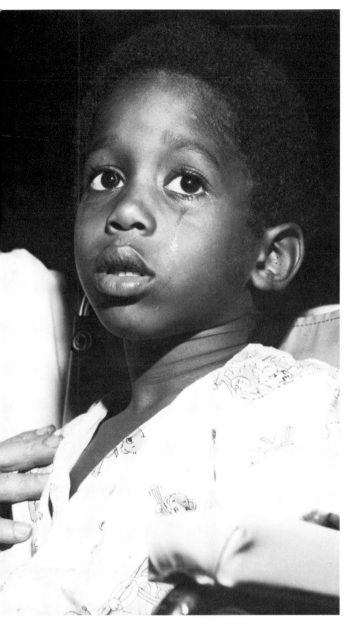

Doctors establish a relationship of trust with each patient.
And, when Danny was in town he could be found at St. Jude
giving encouragement and love to each child.

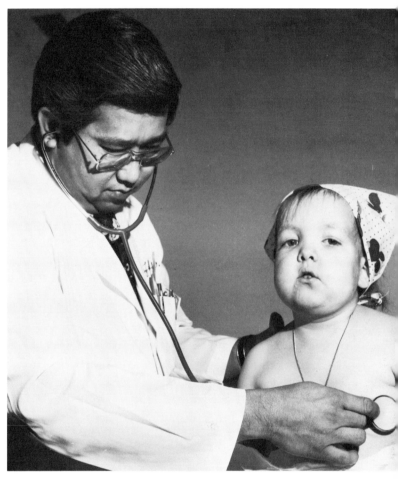

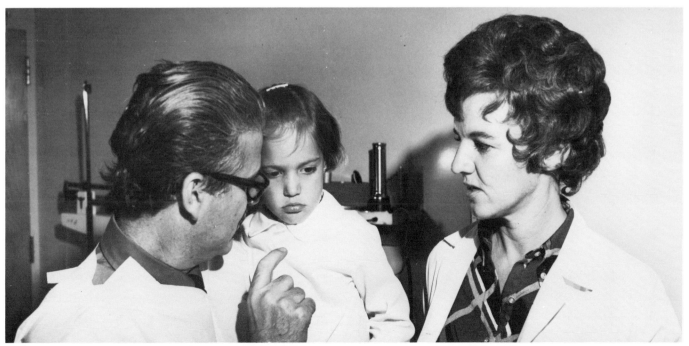

for years and the damage either might do to the child's learning processes and personality, as well as the physical damage that might be done to the child's body.

All these subjects were tackled by a team of psychologists and social workers under the direction of Dr. George W. Marten. Many of the youngsters who were among the first patients at the hospital can today attest to this care and treatment. They are living, free of their crippling disease, and participating in all of the activities of today's teen and adult world.

Pat was admitted to St. Jude in January of 1964 with leukemia. In November of 1966 he was taken off all medication. He returned to the hospital regularly for his check-ups from his home in Harrisburg, Arkansas. In 1970 he graduated with honors from Harrisburg High School and entered college in the fall — just another incoming freshman.

One of the long-term survivors of leukemia is Connie, who left her home in Santa Rita, New Mexico for treatment at St. Jude Hospital. After her initial treatment at the hospital, Connie returned to the home and the life she loved. The hospital pharmacy sent the medicines she needed to her doctor who sent back reports to be entered in her hospital record. And Connie rode the horses that she loved and participated in the life of the little town where she lived.

David entered St. Jude in 1966 when he was

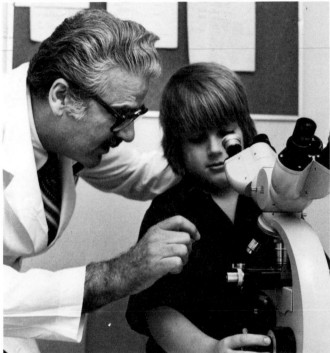

Left: A psychologist talks with a young patient, testing without appearing to, in the attempt to establish patterns that will establish a better quality of life for the youngsters and their parents. Top: Connie Lopez talks with Dr. John Aur on one of her regular visits to the hospital. Above: Bradley Hayne gets a lesson on operating a microscope from Dr. Auer.

"The golden age of St. Jude was ending . . . that initial burst of creativity had paid off . . . now we had to prepare the patients to live."

sixteen years old. His illness was diagnosed as Hodgkin's disease. In 1972 David was married in Memphis where he was working for the Memphis Housing Authority, the organization that had made available the land on which the hospital was built.

Bradley was two years old, had two brothers and a baby sister and lived in Memphis in 1969 when his mother was told that Bradley had leukemia. Their doctor advised that they take him to St. Jude. He said, "They're doing some wonderful things there with children like Bradley." All Bradley's mother could think of was that leukemia was fatal and that her two-year old son would die. Today, he is a healthy, happy well-adjusted teen-ager who goes regularly to St. Jude for follow-up tests only.

Joann spent her 18th birthday at St. Jude Hospital. She was on chemotherapy for two and a half years and has been off all treatment since. At 24, she became the mother of a healthy normal baby girl, six years after being admitted to the hospital. Now she and Starr, her daughter, both return to St. Jude for check-ups. Under the St. Jude study plan the children of patients are entered into the same study . . . as are siblings in some instances. It's a delight for the doctors and medical records staff to see the photographs, side by side, of a healthy mother and daughter.

Many of the patients today are actively in-volved in participating in bike rides and runs that are sponsored by ALSAC to raise funds for the hospital. Rodney, at the age of eight, rode in a Bike-a-thon in Ft. Wayne, Indiana — the entire fifty miles! It took him all day but he completed the race.

Most patients today are maintaining their school work and keeping up with their classmates with the help of home teachers, their families and friends. This is one of the things the hospital staff assures the young patients that they can do. For example, Denice spent most of her junior year of high school in Memphis taking treatments for lymphoma that had been diagnosed at the beginning of the school year. But when it came time to select outstanding juniors and seniors for membership in the National Honor Society, the faculty of the Bossier City, Louisiana school chose 16-year old Denice as one of the group.

At the awards ceremony, the twenty-fifth student to cross the stage, light a ceremonial candle and accept her long-stemmed yellow rose was Denice. She was one of thirty-five students honored for character, leadership, service and scholarship. Her classmates gave her a standing ovation and in Memphis her doctors were also cheering for her. With loving concern, they had arranged her chemotherapy schedule so that she would be able to attend the awards ceremony.

St. Jude Hospital's staff has indeed established

Left: Denice Mason lights her candle at the awards ceremony at her high school in Bossier City, Louisiana. Unlike the long term survivors, Denice was to lose her battle just a year and a half after she was first admitted to St. Jude. But during that time, with the encouragement of her doctors, Denice graduated from high school and enjoyed precious moments spent with her family and friends.

"We don't do just for the patient . . . we do for the family . . . we keep them together."

a quality of life for those children who were to combat the ravaging illnesses that attacked them. And, they have gone a step further — they have challenged their young patients not only to live up to the potential of that quality of life but to exceed it.

After the researchers had found the new procedures that would give many of their patients a chance to live a full and normal life, they were faced with still another challenge. The treatment used had an unfortunate side effect. The body's ability to fight infection was lowered by the cancer-fighting drugs, and the child became very susceptible to infection.

One of these infections was the childhood disease of chicken pox, the other a little-known organism called pneunocystis carinii. Either could be fatal to a child receiving chemotherapy treatments.

The researchers and clinicians at St. Jude found this totally unacceptable. Dr. Mauer expressed the thoughts of the staff when he said, "When you have the child who has his leukemia under control and then he gets an infection and dies, it really tears your heart out."

Early in the 1970's, researchers began work on the problem under the direction of Dr. Walter Hughes, who was in charge of infectious disease control research.

Dr. Sandor Feldman headed the research group studying the caricella-zoster virus, or the chicken pox virus as it is commonly known. He found that shingles, a particularly irritating and painful disease that usually strikes adults, also is caused by the virus that causes chicken pox. No one who has shingles has not first had chicken pox.

Dr. Feldman appealed to the Memphis community for persons who had recovered from shingles to donate blood at the St. Jude Hospital blood bank. He reasoned that the donors would have developed antibodies to the virus. These antibodies would be given to infection-susceptible children who had been exposed to chicken pox. Theoretically, the antibodies in the donor blood would then attack the chicken pox virus in the child.

The day following his public appeal more than thirty Memphis residents showed up at the hospital to donate blood. The serum can be taken and kept almost indefinitely, ready to treat any of the young patients who have been exposed.

And, best of all, the plan worked beautifully and as expected.

The victory over pneumocystis carinii took longer and is considered a "breakthrough," a word seldom used by researchers at St. Jude. In the past a patient who contracted pneumocystis carinii pneumonitis almost always died if not treated. But the only drug that was available at that time had some adverse side effects in some patients — kidney problems, blood sugar problems and skin-sluffing.

While the disease had been known since the late nineteenth century the disease had defied analysis because it could not be grown in laboratories. Dr. Linda Pifer, while at St. Jude Hospital, was the first in the world to grow "the blob" (as she calls it) *in vitro*, or in a culture outside the body. Once the organism was isolated in a culture dish, Dr. Pifer and her associate, Diane Woods, were able to develop a 45-minute blood test to determine if the patient had the disease. This allowed doctors to discover and treat the disease in its early stages.

Using rats as experimental models, the St. Jude researchers found that a combination of drugs, one of them a much-used sulfa drug, not only stopped the pneumocystis pneumonia but it also prevented the disease from occurring. It also stopped other infections, such as ear infections, other pneumonias and upper respiratory infections caused by bacteria.

The drug was tested on 160 children for two years in what is known as a double blind study where neither the patient nor the doctor knows which patient is taking the drug and which the placebo. When the code was broken, the research team learned that none of the children who had been taking the drug had developed pneumocystis carinii. In the other group seventeen of the eighty had developed the disease and had been treated by the conventional method.

Now all St. Jude patients who are at risk for this potential killer are given the antibiotic in daily dosages. This breakthrough brought national recognition to the scientific staff at St. Jude and a word of praise from their friend, Danny Thomas.

"This disease angered our people. I love their anger. They said, 'There has to be a way to stop this pneumonia from getting to these kids.' And, they did it."

The researchers were also not happy with the

150ml
KIMAX
NO. 14000
COHEN
ARMSTRONG
DRUG INTERACTIONS
CANCER
CHEMOTHERAPY
Evans
Schentag
Jusko
APPLIED
PHARMACOKINETICS
GOODMAN and GILMAN
The Pharmacological

"cure rate" that had been established in acute lymphocytic leukemia (ALL). True, chemotherapy seemed to be successful in treating from a third to a half of the children stricken. But the staff was not content to rest on its laurels. If one child still died from ALL, that was one too many.

The ones who died were those who had achieved remission but had relapsed. They sometimes would achieve remission several times only to relapse each time. Some, between five and ten percent, of the new patients would never achieve remission. All would ultimately died. There had to be some way to solve this tragic problem.

In 1971 a team under the guidance of doctors Thomas Avery and DeWayne Roberts began experimental lab tests on mice using an experimental drug called VM-26. The scientific name for the drug is 4'-demethylepipodophyllotoxin 9-(4,6-0-2 thenylidene B-D-glucopyranoside). It is easy to see why the name was shortened to VM-26 for easy reference.

Its source was a common plant found in the woods of the eastern half of the United States,

---

"To take care of a terribly sick child without trying to make his treatment program better would be pretty dismal. It's research that gives us all hope."

"This disease angered our people. I love their anger. They said, 'There has to be a way to stop this pneumonia from getting to these kids.' And, they did it!"

Dr. Gaston Rivera and Dr. Thomas Avery check out the May Apple plant that is the source of the VM-26 medication. This woods is in a Memphis park not two miles from the hospital.

the May Apple. Related closely to the legendary Mandrake of the Bible and folklore, it had been used by the Indians and early settlers both as a medicine and as a poison.

After tests on mice showed favorable results the team of researchers wrote a protocol (a treatment plan) that could be used for the most hopeless of the acute lymphocytic leukemia patients. A team, headed by Dr. Gaston Rivera, who had joined the research team when he first arrived at St. Jude in 1970, began in 1973 a series of treatments on seventeen patients, all of whom had developed a resistance to all other drugs that were used to treat leukemia.

Between 1973 and 1975, these children received VM-26 medication alone. In five of the children the disease abated but none achieved remission. However, the results were encouraging enough for the study to continue. Another drug called cytosine arabinoside, or ara-C, was also showing promising results in tests with laboratory animals. The team decided to try the drugs in combination . . . and they worked even better in combination than singly. The first combination of the drugs was given to thirty-three youngsters in 1975. These children had all stopped responding to conventional treatment. Ten of the group then achieved complete remission and the treatment with the drugs was intensified.

Today all high-risk patients, about twenty percent of all treated, are given a combination of the VM-26/ara-C drugs. The response is most gratifying to the staff at St. Jude — it is one step closer to their goal of working toward a day when no child will be lost to a cancer of any kind.

To aid the research staff with its never-ending flow of data and to give the clinical staff fast and easy access to patient statistics, the hospital quite naturally turned to computer usage in the 1970's. Initially, all work was done on a time-sharing basis through the computer center at Memphis State University.

In March of 1978, a Data General Eclipse mini-computer was installed at the hospital and the Biostatistics Section was established. Chosen to head this division was Dr. Stephen George, a nationally recognized authority — not a physician or a research scientist — but a mathematician.

His staff immediately began converting programs from the university system to its own system. And, since the processing of medical research data can not be easily done by commercial data-base management systems, the Biostatistics Section, working with the medical records department and the pharmacy, developed its own automated system. Their patient-record system requires frequent transfer of data files from one computer system to a second and back again. The transfer is vital between the system used for data acquisition, storage and data-base management to statistical and mathematical analyses.

The system provides monthly summaries of all clinical studies of acute lymphocytic leukemia (ALL) and other analyses for other clinical departments. Monthly summaries also allow a quality-control check on the recorded data and a sequential analysis of results that are particularly important for the "total therapy" studies of ALL.

The patient record files are updated each day and will include the complete research records of all children who have been treated at St. Jude. This will enable the staff to obtain significant data more rapidly for use in developing research programs.

The Biostatistics Section is also engaged in a continuing study of the causation of childhood cancers. This epidemiologic study is being funded by the National Cancer Institute. The study began in 1979 and is planned to extend over a five-year period.

The first phase of the program was to obtain information about the families of children treated for cancer at St. Jude. The first interviews were conducted in September of 1979 and a total of 92 were completed that first year. In interviews with parents, brothers, sisters and children, the family's occupational, environmental and residential history is taken. Information is being obtained by both personal interviews and questionnaires.

This information should bring researchers closer to an understanding of the environmental and hereditary factors of cancer and will help design special treatments for specific patients with similar characteristics.

One example as to how this information would prove invaluable is in the study of twins and, in one case, triplets. When Jeannine was admitted to the research program at St. Jude for treatment of leukemia, two of her siblings were also admitted to the study program. The three are triplets, two girls and one boy. While Jeannine is being treated, her sister and brother are being monitored for any indication of the disease. A part of the files of the Biostatistic Section contains all information to date on Jeannine, her fraternal brother and sister, as well as her three older siblings and her parents.

Below: The Summerlin triplets enjoy a visit with Danny. When Jeannine was admitted to the hospital for treatment for leukemia, her sister and brother were also entered into the study. Neither sibling has shown any evidence of the disease but their participation in the study is very helpful to the researchers.

The 1970's saw a need for additional space for the animal research quarters. Housed in a 21,500 square foot area in the basement of the original building, the space had been utilized to its optimum but was still not sufficient for all the research programs that the basic scientists in that area needed to conduct. Also, a more specialized facility was needed for the more complex studies that were being considered for the future.

Plans were drawn up for a highly sophisticated laboratory with a cost estimate of more than five million dollars. Half of the funds were raised through a solicitation of Memphis businessmen. John Ford Canale, Memphis attorney and member of the Board of Governors since its beginning, was named chairman for the drive. He formed a committee of forty businessmen, each responsible for contacting only three or four others. Within three months, their goal of two and a half million dollars was reached. The largest single contributor was the Plough Foundation with its gift of $250,000.

In 1979, St. Jude received a grant of 1.9 million dollars from the National Cancer Institute, one of the largest grants ever made to a single institution. A challenge grant of $500,000 was received from the Kresge Foundation of Michigan. These assured the slightly over five million dollars that would be needed to build and equip the center.

June 25, 1981 a dedication and open house was held at the building, constructed just behind the hospital. Then it became the province of the research staff. Few people other than the scientists and employees of the facility now enter the area. Nothing, absolutely nothing, goes into some of the areas designated as "clean" areas without protection or a sterilization treatment. Exit from these areas is through a door at the other end into a "dirty" corridor. There is no retracing one's steps since the doors by which one enters contain no handle on the inside!

The animals and the people who work with them must be protected at all times from cross-infection. Contamination can destroy a research project that has been on-going for weeks, months, or years.

The building is said to be the finest, most sophisticated center of its kind in the country. The increased space and increased technology will enable the researchers, under the direction of Jon Garcia, to expand their research into different drug treatments and their study of the various viruses.

The staff of St. Jude Hospital is representative of all regions of the United States and most foreign countries. It consists of 95 full-time faculty members, 12 part-time faculty members, 41

Top: Dedication of the new building. On Danny Thomas' left, seated, is John Ford Canale, head of the drive to raise two and a half million dollars from Memphis businessmen. The amount was raised by Canale and a forty-member team within three months. Above: In the old days of the hospital goat blood samples were needed for laboratory experiments. The goats were kept in a corral miles north of Memphis and when Dr. Avery and his team needed blood samples they picked up their lassos and headed for the corral. Left: All the newest in electronic controls for the just-opened facility.

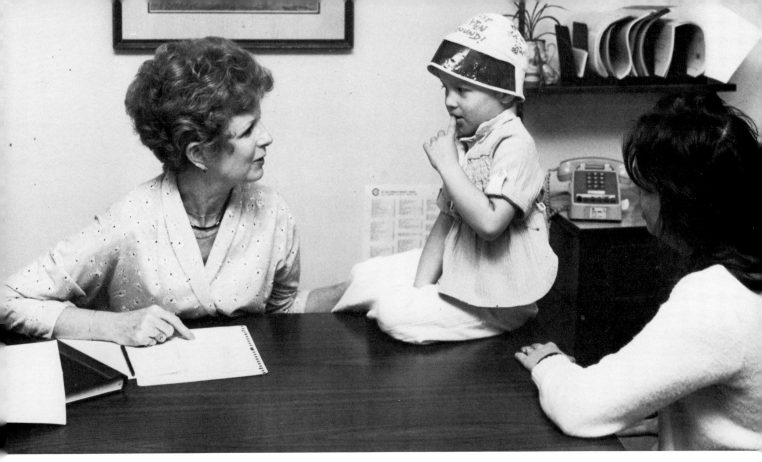

"It's just one big happy family, the love that goes on between the staff and the children. I've seen it nowhere else."

Upper: There's always time during the day to answer a child's questions. Center and lower: On a summer weekend, the staff stages a bazaar to raise money for the hospital.

fellows and trainees, 11 research assistants, 15 clinical staff assistants and 66 registered nurses.

And no history of St. Jude Children's Research Hospital would be complete without a word for the supporting cast of hundreds . . . the hospital employees who support the doctors and the scientists in all areas.

The nursing staff is dedicated to its work. One nurse practitioner sums it up, "I've been here ten years. I came immediately after I got out of school and was going to work a year or so to get some experience and move on. I've never left. St. Jude is a place where we can relieve the families of at least part of the burden they have to bear."

That same dedication is found in the clinical and basic research laboratory assistants . . . in the clerical staff . . . medical records . . . accounting . . . admissions . . . purchasing . . . computer services . . . housekeeping . . . personnel . . . audiovisual . . . public relations . . . scientific editing . . . grants management . . . cafeteria . . . and the administrative staff.

It makes no difference if a person works in an area where there is constant contact with the children or if the only contact might be in the corridors or at lunch in the cafeteria. It's just one big happy family . . . giving love to the children who come to St. Jude seeking their help.

And the staff does not end its work with the close of an eight hour shift. The employees of St. Jude help in many of the fund-raising endeavors of ALSAC. Nurses go to places like Peoria, Illinois to ride in Bike-a-thons. Many are on call for any event that occurs in the Memphis area . . . they work bike rides, runs and telethons. And, once a year the staff has its own major fund-raising event . . . the Employees Bazaar.

The event is staged one Saturday in the summer and the employees and their families, the patients and their families, and friends of all enjoy the day. There are games of chance, raffles, things to buy, lots to eat and a great deal of hilarity. Some people dream all year of this day when the chance comes to "dunk" a staff member in the waters of the dunk tank.

A great deal of planning and effort goes into making the day a success and each year in the past few years over $20,000 has been raised for "their" hospital!

Supporting the hospital staff is the volunteer staff . . . a group of extremely dedicated people. The first volunteers were the Ladies of St. Jude who were organized even before the hospital opened. In the early days of the hospital, the

"St. Jude is extraordinary not only for the brilliance of its research but also for the warmth of its care, as thousands of children and their parents from many countries can testify."

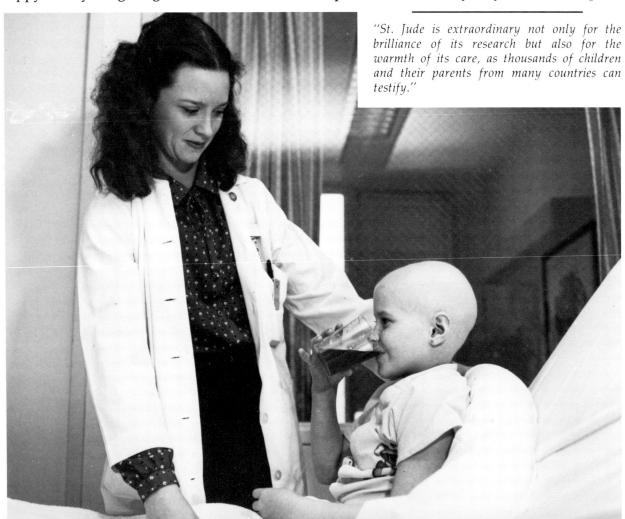

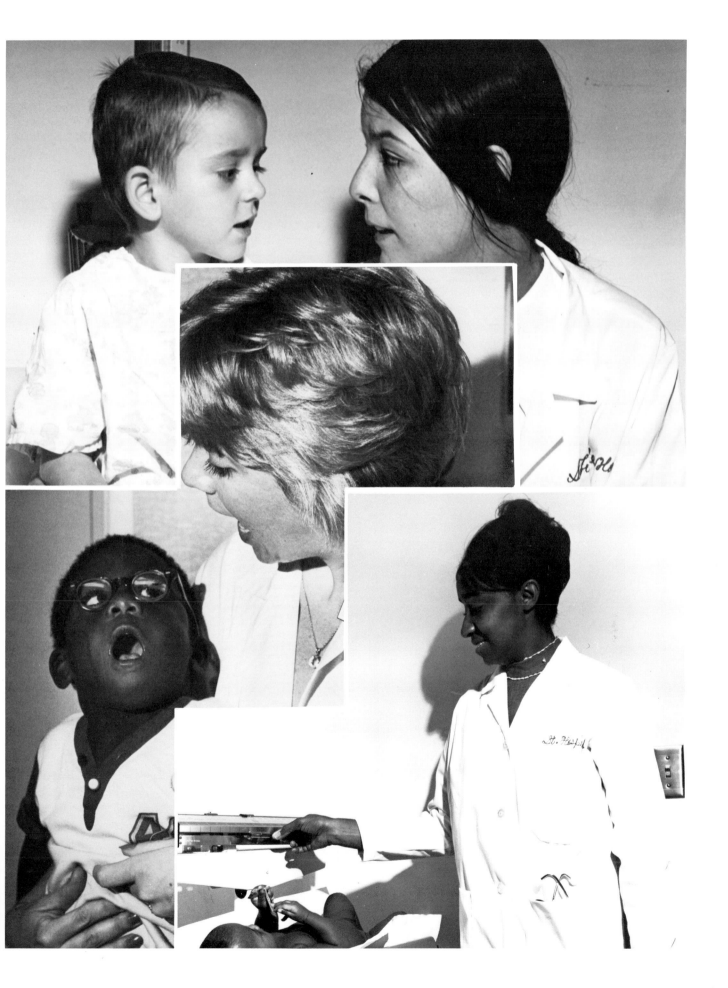

volunteers worked with the children — reading to them, telling them stories, taking the parents to and from the hospital and shopping. Others worked in the office area alongside the doctors and scientists.

The Ladies of St. Jude organized themselves and maintained their own schedules. They also raised funds for the playroom and other hospital equipment.

In 1972, the Wives Club was formed to serve as volunteers. Their husbands worked in all areas of the hospital. Some were doctors, some scientists, some worked in the offices and the maintenance departments.

In 1973, a decision was made that a volunteer director who served on a part time basis did not have the time to handle the increasing volume of work necessary as the hospital continued to grow. A full-time director, Roberta Carder, went to work at the hospital in December of 1973 and is still on the job.

The volunteers today are divided into three groups — and all work very well together. There are the original Ladies of St. Jude, several of whom have been working every week since the hospital opened; the Wives Club; and the Auxiliary Group. In the summer, teen volunteers from the Red Cross are assigned to help in the hospital.

Volunteers work in all departments with the exception of the inpatient care area. Their purpose is not to replace a paid employee, but to supplement services where a paid employee cannot be. They give tours at the hospital, do clerical work, type, file, work with slides in the labs, work in radiology, write thank you letters, stuff envelopes, sort materials and anything else that is needed at the moment. They work in the hospital and also in the ALSAC offices.

The volunteers also operate and maintain a gift shop in the hospital lobby with the profits being returned to the hospital; they arrange entertainment for the patients; they work at local fund raising events including the Danny Thomas Memphis Golf Classic and the annual telethon.

One special task that several enjoy doing is helping doctors who arrive at the hospital from all over the world to study at St. Jude get settled in the community. They help with every facet including obtaining drivers licenses to finding a place to live and enrolling the children in schools.

An average of seventy active volunteers work each month at St. Jude and at least twenty percent of these have been involved with the hospital since its opening.

The Ladies of St. Jude also stage a major fashion show each year to raise funds for the hospital. Professional models are used to show the women's fashions, but their escorts might include the Memphis police director, the basketball coach from Memphis State University, a city councilman, a mayor and several of the doctors from St. Jude Hospital.

During this remarkable growth period, St. Jude Hospital and its staff did not forget its responsibility to share the knowledge gained by its research staff with the rest of the medical community.

Many St. Jude staff members hold appointments to the faculty of the University of Tennessee Center for the Health Sciences. In addition to their teaching responsibilities, these scientists often join in collaborative research efforts with investigators at the University.

St. Jude has established affiliation with the Methodist Medical Center in Peoria, Illinois; T. C. Thompson Children's Hospital in Chattanooga, Tennessee; and St. Elizabeth Hospital Medical Center in Youngstown, Ohio. These hospitals follow the same protocols in their treatment of children as those developed at St. Jude and their patients participate in studies conducted at St. Jude. These hospitals and St. Jude exchange personnel also for periods of in-service education.

St. Jude Hospital also hosts an annual two-day symposium for referring physicians to acquaint them with the facilities and the staff of the hospital and to familiarize them with the most recent research findings and the current methods used for the care and treatment of children with cancer. Since the very beginning seminar was held in 1967 for physicians who had referred patients to the hospital and were responsible for their follow-up care, the symposium has grown to include doctors and nurses with a particular interest in oncology.

There are also many opportunities for advanced education at St. Jude Hospital. Qualified physicians, nurses, predoctoral students and post-doctoral scientists may receive advanced

Classes and seminars are held in the St. Jude Hospital auditorium.

training in one of the hospital's clinical or biomedical programs. Or they may participate in interdisciplinary programs that combine clinical specialties with one or more of the basic biomedical sciences.

The aim of this program is to educate trainees in the principles of sound research and to involve them in the problems of patient management. The scope of training benefits from cooperative agreements with the University of Tennessee Center for the Health Sciences and several Memphis general hospitals.

St. Jude also offers a three-year American Medical Association approved post graduate training program for physicians who wish to specialize in pediatrics. Postdoctoral fellows with an M.D. or Ph.D. degree are offered from one to three years of advanced training in a basic, biomedical science (such as biochemistry, immunology, pharmacology or virology) or a clinical specialty (such as cardiopulmonary diseases, pathology, surgery, diagnostic radiology, radiotheraphy or pharmaceuticals). Under the guidance of a St. Jude professor, fellows select and carry out an original research project. Additionally, through attendance at

weekly seminars and work-shops, they acquire an appreciation of biological and medical problems outside their major fields of interest.

Through a cooperative agreement with the University of Tennessee, St. Jude's biochemistry, virology, immunology, and pharmacology divisions offer programs leading to the Ph.D. degree. After a year of formal classroom study at the university, these students select a major professor on the St. Jude Hospital faculty and begin a research project under that staff member's supervision. Predoctoral trainees are given wide exposure to the techniques and problems of cancer research through regularly scheduled seminars and contact with senior investigators.

These seminars provide a forum for the exchange of ideas and information among staff members, visiting investigators and fellows. Held regularly at the hospital auditorium are:

INSTITUTIONAL SEMINAR — a weekly presentation by a distinguished visiting scientist or physician.

FACULTY SEMINAR — a weekly presentation by a St. Jude staff member on his or her field of interest.

INFORMAL WEEKLY PRESENTATIONS —

of research or discussion of journal articles by department members.

HEMATOLOGY-ONCOLOGY REPORT — solid tumor grand rounds. A weekly presentation of hospitalized patients and an in-depth multidisciplinary discussion of selected oncology cases.

HOUSE-STAFF LECTURE SERIES — RESIDENT'S CONFERENCE — weekly presentations of clinical topics by trainees, in-house staff and occasionally visiting physicians.

St. Jude Hospital also offers the Karnofsky Fellowship in cancer research. The fellowship was established at St. Jude in memory of Dr. David A. Karnofsky, an early member of the hospital's Scientific Advisory Board. It is awarded annually and acknowledges a physician or basic scientist who has advanced beyond the postdoctoral level and is pursuing training in basic or clinical cancer research.

Dr. Karnofsky's career, while chief of the Medical Oncology Service at Memorial Hospital and head of the Division of Chemotherapy Research at Sloan-Kettering Institute was dedicated to cancer research. His findings were instrumental in establishing the importance of chemotheraphy in the treatment of cancer. More than a dozen scientists from Chile, Switzerland, Brazil, England, Japan and the United States have trained under this fellowship.

The Leon Journey Fellowship in biomedical research and the Robbie Simpson Fellowship in cancer nursing are also offered. Competition for these three fellowships is both national and international, and awardees are selected on a highly competitive basis.

The latest training program to be added at St. Jude is a new pediatrics program developed in 1980 by St. Jude Children's Research Hospital, the University of Tennessee Center for the Health Sciences and LeBonheur Children's Hospital. It is a unique residency program where graduates spend three years in Memphis completing their pediatric education by attending conferences and treating patients in all three institutions.

More than three hundred of the better medical school graduates applied for this "Pediatric Residency — Memphis." Only fourteen of the group could be accepted for the first year of the program which began July 1, 1981.

This residency is unique in that it combines the clinical education, research and service facilities of the three institutions to create a truly exceptional experience for physicians who want to specialize in health problems in children.

Dr. Alvin Mauer feels it is both an obligation and a responsibility for St. Jude to participate in conferences and to share the knowledge that has been obtained at St. Jude. Any week of the year will find doctors and staff members, sometimes by the dozens, traveling both near and far to participate in seminars and conferences. And, in any one year, visiting lecturers and scientists lecture at St. Jude from as many as twenty foreign countries.

Members of the St. Jude staff yearly give lectures and present papers at hospitals, universities and research facilities in more than half the states in the United States and as many foreign countries. In one year they attended and made presentations at scientific meetings in Greece, India, the Netherlands, Australia, Costa Rica, Belgium and the USSR.

In taking the "gospel of St. Jude" procedures around the world, the staff has cut across all bar-

riers — the politics of a country are unimportant to the exchange of scientific knowledge.

Danny Thomas recalls that shortly after the hospital opened he was talking with President John F. Kennedy and he asked the President if he felt that it would be a good idea to invite the heads of state of other countries to visit St. Jude. John Kennedy's answer was, "No. Invite the doctors, the scientists to study with you." That advice was followed.

Even with countries where our diplomatic relations have been somewhat strained at times there has been an exchange of knowledge with the top scientists of the countries. As early as 1972 Dr. Granoff told the story of St. Jude to scientists in the USSR. In 1979, scientists from the USSR including Dr. Demitri Lvov, director of Ivanovsky Institute of Virology in Moscow, and Dr. Tamaz Peradze, director of the Pasteur Institute of Epidemiology and Microbiology in Leningrad, were in Memphis studying influenza viruses at St. Jude Hospital.

Also in 1979, Dr. Mauer was one of three American physicians invited to serve as an advisory board for cancer research for the King Faisal Specialist Hospital and Research Center in Saudi Arabia. He also made a trip to Libya where he was one of a group of doctors invited to participate in an international seminar. The seminar was held to commemorate the International Year of the Child and its focus was child health.

St. Jude research programs are in use in East Germany behind the Iron Curtain. The instructions to scientists and doctors are to use treatments "according to the Memphis plan."

Following the breakthrough in scientific communication with Russia, East Germany and Libya, there remained only the People's Republic of China. In 1972, shortly after China opened its doors to the rest of the world, Dr. Robert Webster, director of influenza studies at St. Jude, was invited to China to address the Chinese Medical Academy in Peking and to assist Chinese scientists in establishing epidemiologic studies of influenza viruses.

This visit initiated a research collaboration that has included reciprocal laboratory visits and plans for training postdoctoral investigators. In 1981, through a fellowship from the World Health Organization, a virologist from the National Vaccine and Serum Institute in Peking began working with Dr. Webster.

In 1980, Dr. Alvin Mauer visited China as a guest of the Chinese Academy of Medical Sciences. He was accompanied on his trip by his son, Timothy, who speaks fluent Chinese. Dr. Mauer lectured in Peking, Shanghai, Hangchow and Suchow. As a result of this visit, St. Jude

The sign outside the Shanghai No. 1 Medical School Hospital reads "We welcome with enthusiasm the chairman of the American Society of Hematology, Dr. Mauer, to visit our hospital." Outside to personally welcome Dr. Mauer on his visit to the hospital are the chairperson of the department of pediatrics and the director of the division of hematology.

Drs. Granoff and Webster discuss ongoing research with visiting Chinese virologists.

Hospital, in conjunction with the Chinese Academy of Sciences, has established three special fellowships for postdoctoral trainees from China. One is in biochemistry, one in immunology and one in virology.

In 1981, Dr. Marvin Fishman of the immunology division of St. Jude was one of thirty prominent Western scientists who participated in the Second International Symposium on RNA in Developmental Biology, held in Peking. At the invitation of the Chinese Academy of Science, Dr. Fishman joined other scientists from the United States and Western Europe, along with fifty-three representatives from China, for a five-day symposium which was co-sponsored by The People's Republic of China and the Rockefeller Foundation.

These contacts have resulted in Chinese scientists and physicians coming to the United States to train at St. Jude Hospital.

American scientists can also learn from the Chinese — one example is the meticulous epidemiologic studies of cancer done by the Chinese. Also, American scientists will have an opportunity to test new cancer drugs, such as herringtonin, a plant alkaloid used in China to treat patients with acute leukemia.

But most of all it closes the last gap in the world-wide exchange of scientific knowledge.

While relations with China were being established, St. Jude's contacts with other countries were also being furthered. In 1979, a group of European doctors visited the United States to study three institutions. One of the three was St. Jude Children's Research Hospital.

And the following year four members of the St. Jude staff were invited to attend the International Society for Pediatric Oncology in Budapest where they told of their studies with VM-26 and ara-C treatment of leukemia.

Children also come to St. Jude Hospital for treatment from the four corners of the world.

A missionary family from Pennsylvania was living and working in an isolated jungle in Paraguay. Their only access to the outside world was a dirt road to the highway and a small aircraft strip three miles away.

The couple's 14-year old daughter was hemorrhaging and they had to get her to the capitol, Asuncion. But rain had closed the dirt road. Using a tractor and trailer, outfitted with a makeshift hammock bed, and guided by radio communication, they managed to get Pamela to the

Dr. Fishman with colleagues at the Institute of Genetics in Beijing, China.

capitol city where Dr. Claudio Prieto, who had trained at St. Jude Hospital, diagnosed Pamela with acute lymphocytic leukemia.

It had taken seven and a half hours to make their way from their village to the capitol city some 200 miles away. But it took less than twenty-four hours for Pamela and her father to make the trip to St. Jude Hospital. Chemotherapy was prescribed and Pamela was treated with VM-26. Soon she was in remission and enjoying American television in her motel room in Memphis.

Hugo was abandoned by his mother soon after

his birth in Guatemala. He became a ward of the state and a group of volunteer relief workers from Tennessee, called simply "The Farm" became custodians of little Hugo.

When he developed leukemia, The Farm volunteers took him to St. Jude Hospital. That was in April of 1978. One of The Farm's members tells about the youngster, "He's really very strong. He withstood both chicken pox and pneumonia while getting his leukemia therapy. He's a real inspiration to us."

Two years later Hugo was still in remission and well on his way to recovery. Plans are that he will be returned to Guatemala where he will live in the camp operated by Plenty (The Farm's non-profit relief organization) and grow strong to be able to help others in his country as he has been helped.

Daniel, a teenager from Bern, Switzerland, still has his right arm and the use of it. Daniel had osteogenic sarcoma, a malignant primary tumor of the bone. A few years ago the only treatment would have been amputation since bone cancer spreads so rapidly.

———————

Above: Danny Thomas and Dr. Mauer with one of the color photographs of St. Jude Hospital, signed by co-workers, that hangs in offices of doctors, scientists and technicians around the world, who share the knowledge and experience learned at St. Jude with their new associates.

Left: Pamela Heckart and her mother. Following treatment with VM-26, Pamela went into remission. Her family moved to Memphis and she enrolled in school. But, after a year, the leukemia returned and Pamela and her doctors lost the battle. A Memphis newspaper interview quoted Pam, "I just hope that maybe God wants me to go ahead and live. But, if He doesn't, I'm ready."

But Daniel's doctor in Bern told his parents about a doctor he had seen perform surgery on this type cancer at Memorial Sloan-Kettering Cancer Institute in New York. Only nine doctors in the world performed this surgery — six were in the United States and three outside the United States. Dr. Bhaskar N. Rao, the doctor who had performed the surgery in New York, had joined the staff of St. Jude Hospital in November of 1980 as chief of surgery.

Daniel and his father flew to Memphis where Dr. Rao did the complex surgery necessary to remove the tumor and still save the use of Daniel's arm. Following chemotherapy treatment, Daniel was ready to return home in the spring of the next year with two good arms and a newly acquired taste for hamburgers and root beer.

Along with exporting knowledge, St. Jude also exports people, people like Pamela's doctor in Paraguay.

Many doctors in cancer centers across the nation and in some foreign countries hang over their desks a color photograph of St. Jude Children's Research Hospital signed by all the friends he or she worked with at St. Jude. The framed document holds a prominent place on many office walls around the world. And the knowledge gained at St. Jude is shared by this doctor with his new colleagues and the enthusiasm learned at St. Jude is also happily shared with his new associates.

It's a never-ending circle, emanating from St. Jude Hospital in Memphis, Tennessee, founded just twenty years ago to fulfill a vow to St. Jude Thaddeus, and going, truly, around the world.

Twenty Years Later . . . St. Jude Today

Today the main entrance to St. Jude Children's Research Hospital is still past the statue of St. Jude Thaddeus and into the outer lobby of the original Star of Hope building. The outside walls at the front of this building are covered with white ceramic plaques lettered in gold that acknowledge early memorial donations to the hospital. The end walls of the inner lobby are also covered with similar plaques. Inside this lobby children and parents may be waiting for a driver to take them back to their motel, or for a parent or friend to bring a car up to the entrance. Before going into the inner lobby a visitor begins to have a feeling that this is indeed a very special place.

Once inside the inner doors, it is advisable not to let one's attention wander from the immediate. This is the rotunda of the original structure and it is now used as a waiting room for the outpatient clinic. One glance will tell that it is a children's world. Most who are waiting for a call to the various treatment areas are acting as children do — they are unguided missiles — and an adult would do well to watch his every step.

Comfortable couches and chairs are scattered throughout the lobby. At one side is a play area for the especially active. There are books for those who choose to be less active, and games. One wall holds a display case of Boehm ceramics, given to the hospital by Helen Boehm for the children and their parents to enjoy. Next to the reception desk is one of the busiest spots in the lobby — the gift shop, manned by volunteers. Most of the youngsters check in to browse through the toys and gifts displayed there.

And usually, before a child leaves the hospital, a small purchase is made in the gift shop. More often than not, it is a gift to take home to a brother or sister. And, while there, the children chat with the volunteer who is on duty. She knows many of

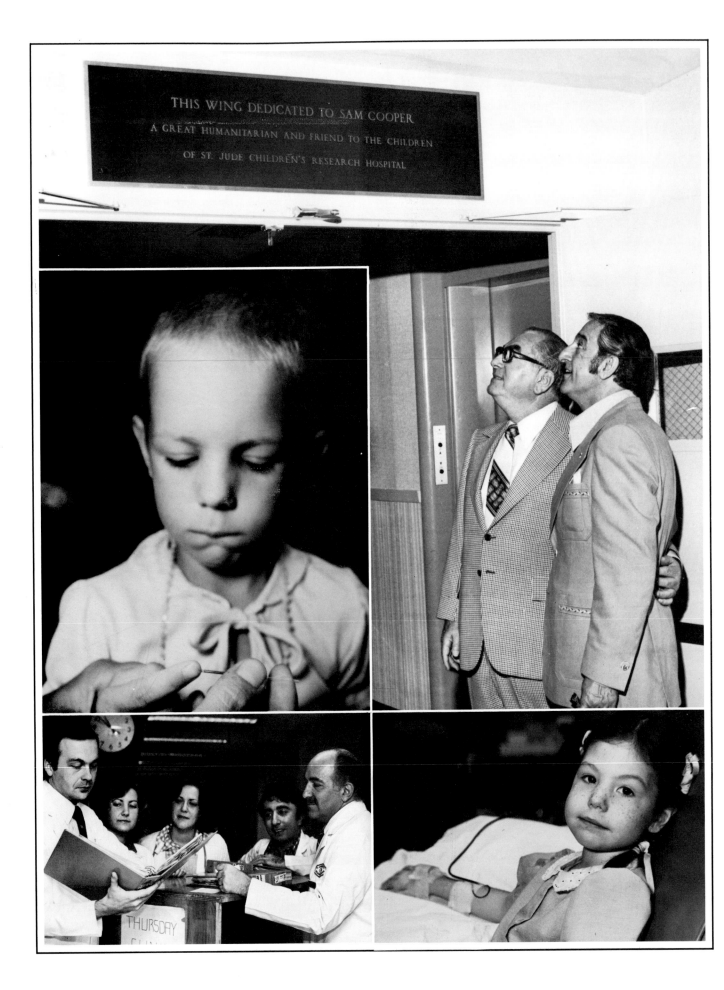

THIS WING DEDICATED TO SAM COOPER
A GREAT HUMANITARIAN AND FRIEND TO THE CHILDREN
OF ST. JUDE CHILDREN'S RESEARCH HOSPITAL

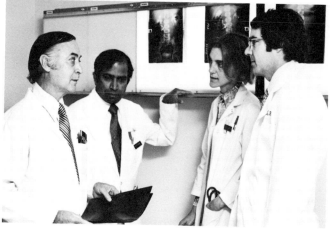

"I've never worked in an institution before where the whole totality of the hospital is to keep children alive and healthy."

Top: Waiting in the rotunda to be called into the outpatient wing for treatment. Above: The Neuroblastoma team discusses a patient's treatment. From the left: Drs. Omar Hustu, Mahesh Kumar, Ann Hayes and Alexander Green. Lower left: Danny Thomas and Sam Cooper check the plaque dedicating the outpatient wing to Cooper. Remainder of page — activities relative to the new wing.

them by name, what they are being treated for and how they are doing. The gift shop volunteers worry about the youngsters and keep close tabs on their progress.

The wing to the left, which was the original inpatient ward, was converted into an outpatient clinic, after the tower was built. It is filled with children — in the treatment rooms and waiting in the colorful corridors. On the wall of the corridor are bulletin boards that are covered solid with snapshots, mostly school pictures, of the children who come in for treatment. They are encouraged to pin up a new picture when they have one taken.

In 1968, only about fifteen to twenty patients a day were treated in the outpatient department. Today will see closer to a hundred and fifty treated each weekday.

There are twenty-nine treatment rooms in the wing which is divided into three sections — general pediatrics, hematology and oncology. The wing is dedicated to Sam Cooper, a Memphian and retired president of Humko Products. Mr. Cooper headed a fund-raising drive in Memphis that raised a total of four million two hundred thousand dollars for cancer research at St.

Jude and the University of Tennessee Center for the Health Sciences. The money was raised in just three and a half months!

Also in the wing is the dental clinic — bright, cheerful and colorful. Each child is regularly examined and treated in this clinic. Children in the general pediatrics program also see the dentist as a part of an educational program to teach them how to take care of their teeth and the correct way to use a toothbrush.

An opthamologist is available one day a week as are ear, nose and throat specialists. Dieticians are also in the area for any special problems the children may have.

The original playroom donated by the Ladies of St. Jude when the hospital first opened has been converted into a medicine room. It is filled with comfortable lounge chairs for children and their parents while they are receiving intravenous medication, which takes quite a long time. But each child has a toy to distract it, a gift from one of several organizations like the Altrusa Club, whose members started in 1980 bringing bags of toys, puzzles and games to the hospital for the children. They have also donated magazines for the younger children as well as magazines, a tape player and music tapes for the Teen Room, adjacent to the medicine room.

In the late 1970's some of the teen patients went to Sandy Vogel Lewis, executive secretary of the Board of Governors and chief "trouble-shooter" in many areas of the hospital, to ask if there could be a separate room for them apart from the medicine room. It hurt them to see the little children receiving their medication — they suffered with them because they each remembered all too well how they, themselves, suffered in taking their medication.

Because of that, and because their interests were so different from the younger children, they wondered if they might have their own "world" — particularly since they had to spend so much of their time at the hospital.

Sandy accepted the challenge and the teens have their room. It contains a television set, a bumper pool table, backgammon games, a tape player, books and magazines. Asked how she did it, Sandy will just say, "Oh, I called a few people — and they really wanted to help . . .".

In 1981, a young man named John Freight spent some time in the hospital adding a colorful

CHILDREN ARE CHILDREN . . .

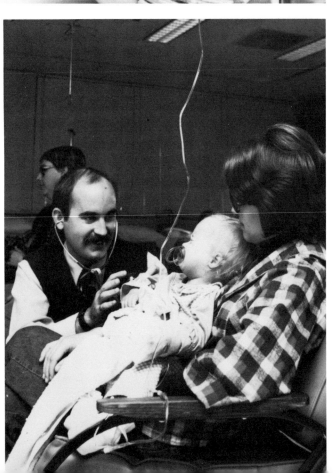

...EVEN AT ST. JUDE

mural to the Teen Room. John is an Atlanta resident who started in the mid-70's to fulfill a grand plan in his life — to make hospitals more colorful. He has painted more than six hundred murals in twenty-six hospitals in the United States and in Europe.

Outside the medicine room is a play area where the children can play, or sit in the sun, if they feel inclined.

Adjacent to the lobby is the pharmacy. Once a child is accepted as a patient at St. Jude, all drugs and medication are furnished free for as long as the medication is needed. When the child returns home to be treated by his own doctor, according to the protocol outlined by his doctors at St. Jude, the drugs are shipped from the pharmacy to his doctor for administration to the patient.

The pharmacy also maintains a complete record of all medication the patient has received, or is receiving, and a computer print-out will give the pharmacist and doctors this information in an instant.

Just at the entrance to the wing directly opposite the outpatient clinic is the inter-faith chapel, which contains symbols and prayer books for all religions. Mass is said in the chapel every Friday and it is open at all times for the hospital staff, for patients and parents.

The chapel is dedicated to the memory of Samuel Cardinal Stritch, Danny Thomas' friend and mentor from the Roman Catholic Church, and Metropolitan Antony Bashir, Archbishop of New York and all North America for the Syrian-Antiochian Orthodox Church.

Two christenings and two weddings have been held in the chapel. Susan was the first patient to be married there. When she was taking her pre-enrollment physical for college, she found that she had leukemia. Hours later she was accepted at St. Jude. In less than a month she was in remission and three years later she was about to be married.

"I wouldn't be here," she reasoned, "if it weren't for this hospital and these people. There couldn't be a more appropriate place for me to be married." She, the groom, their families and friends traveled five hundred miles to the hospital for the ceremony, held on August 16, 1974.

The staff of St. Jude gave her a surprise reception in the cafeteria and one of the staff recalls, "I don't know who cried the most — her parents or her doctors and nurses. We were all so happy for her."

And, just to keep it all in the family, in 1977, Susan, then 24 years old, asked Danny Thomas

"They're all my buddies — they're all beautiful people. We got those who care behind us. It's a way of thanking God for their good health and the health of their kids."

to be the godfather of her first child!

Just outside the entrance to the chapel is a memorial plaque listing the Project 400 Donors. It lists the people who donated money to Danny's dream long before it became a reality. Most of the names are from the show business community or are of Lebanese ancestry. Some still serve on the Board of Governors of the hospital . . . and many individuals and groups

"I wouldn't be here if it weren't for this hospital and these people. There couldn't be a more appropriate place for me to be married."

Top left: Danny and Rose Marie Thomas in the chapel just after the hospital was opened. Lower left: Susan Darlene Bailey became the first patient to be married in the chapel. She and her groom, Michael Robinson, leave the chapel through a veil of rice thrown by their families and the St. Jude staff. Right: Three years later Susan asks Danny if he will be the godfather of her first child.

are still actively involved in raising money for St. Jude Hospital.

Beyond the chapel are double doors leading into the virology laboratories, the first area of research that was established in the hospital. Halfway down the wing is Dr. Allan Granoff's office — located in the very same place that he selected for it when he joined the staff in 1962!

Dr. Granoff is Associate Director for Basic Research and Chairman of the Virology Division. The scientists working with him are in agreement with Granoff that research is a "hard tough business." And also that it demands of those involved a creative drive that he calls "innovative creativity."

One of the most important studies underway in this area is an influenza virus study under the direction of Dr. Robert Webster. Dr. Webster is a director of the World Health Organization in Geneva, Switzerland, and St. Jude was appointed as a focal point for some of the major animal influenza virus studies done in the world. Studies done here will hopefully allow scientists to recognize approaching world-wide influenza strains and be able to control them with newly-developed vaccines.

The next wing contains the neuropsychology department and the psychology and psychiatric laboratories. In this area the doctors and researchers are involved in both the treatment and study of the emotional problems created for a youngster stricken with catastrophic illness. They work with the children — and their parents and siblings — to help make the life that the treatment at St. Jude has given them as emotionally trouble-free as possible.

This wing is dedicated to the Alpha Phi Omega fraternity, a group of young men from the University of Tennessee at Martin who give up their spring break each year to walk the 132 miles to St. Jude Hospital, pushing wheelbarrows and collecting money for St. Jude along the way. In 1971, the first year they made the walk they collected $17,000. Ten years later they were bringing in over $50,000 a year!

Lower left: Dr. Allan Granoff meets informally with members of his research team. Lower right: Dr. Robert Webster is engaged in continuing study of influenza strain viruses and works with leading researchers from around the world.

Young men from the Alpha Phi Omega fraternity from the University of Tennessee at Martin take a 132-mile walk to Memphis collecting money along the way for St. Jude. Left photo shows the first efforts in 1971. Ten years later they had picked up a police escort and additional volunteers.

Directly behind the rotunda waiting room is the admissions area and the blood bank. The blood bank still accepts donations from individuals, and drives are held among the hospital employees yearly for blood donations. All who can give willingly because they have seen what a donation of a pint of blood can do in the treatment of a child.

Now, too, the hospital works closely with the American Red Cross. One weekend a youngster with a very rare blood type needed blood. The Red Cross found the necessary supply in Iowa and had it flown into the hospital. That weekend the doctors used a supply of blood that would have cost the family, had there been a charge, a total of almost $40,000. This blood was furnished to the child at no cost to the parents, and because of the dedication of the American Red Cross and the hospital staff, the child is alive and well today!

To the left of the admissions area is the diagnostic radiology unit bearing the contemporary name of Diagnostic Imaging department. All X-ray work is done in this area as well as all ultra-scan work. The hospital is a co-owner of a CAT-scanner, one of eight in the Memphis area. It is located at St. Joseph Hospital, immediately next door to St. Jude, but all monitoring equipment is duplicated in the St. Jude laboratories. Each hospital paid half the cost of the CAT-scanner, a staggering total amount of $840,000.

Along the corridors of this wing, as well as other areas where the children receive treatment, are colorful murals of a child's favorite cartoon characters. An art class from a local high school donated a year of their time after school and on week-ends to paint the caricatures on the walls of this area. The children are delighted with the familiar faces that help distract them as they wait for a sometime unfamiliar examination or treatment.

Beyond this area lies the radiation therapy department. Machines here are connected directly to a computer that is the hub for both diagnostic radiation and radiation therapy. Many man hours are saved by the computer which determines the exact area to be radiated and the proper amount of radiation needed in each treatment.

The wall treatment here was designed and painted by David Hopkins of Columbus, Ohio, who was sent to the hospital by Wendy's Inter-

Crayons and paper help pass the time waiting for radiation therapy.

national to help brighten an awesome and sometimes frightening area. There is also a separate waiting room in this wing where the children and their parents can relax in a quiet atmosphere while awaiting their turn for treatment.

The next area contains the clinical laboratories, where all clinical research is conducted that involves either an inpatient or an outpatient. All urinalysis, bacteriology, hematology, special chemistry tests are administered and evaluated in the hospital. Nothing goes out of the building for reading or evaluation. The only time tests are sent outside is if a doctor should want a second opinion from a colleague.

At the end of the corridor is the blood collecting laboratory. Each child who comes to St. Jude for treatment must have what is called a blood stick. This is one of the first tests administered each visit and it consists of the removal of a small amount of blood either from the finger or the arm. The doctor must see the lab results on this test before he or she talks with the patient or the parents.

To expedite this study, the hematology lab has a Coulter Counter machine. A technician takes the blood from the finger stick, mixes it with a saline solution and runs it through the machine. In just forty-five seconds, it gives a total readout of seven different results of study. This would take a lab technician over a half hour to complete the same study.

Since more than a hundred and twenty-five tests are done a day, this machine frees the technician for more immediate studies. And, it reduces the waiting time for the patients and the doctors immeasurably.

Since the blood stick test is the first that the children receive, the personnel who staff that area are especially sensitive to the moods of the children. They know the regular patients by name, they know about their brothers and sisters, their pets, their hobbies, their favorite school subjects. And, everyone gets involved in making this first test as easy as possible for the child.

One day when Danny Thomas was in the hospital visiting with the patients and staff, he stopped by the blood collecting room to find a

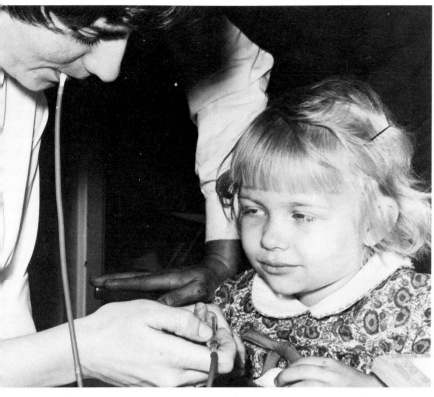

"If you can do something to deal with a child's suffering, it's a very uplifting experience."

From the momentary nick of a blood stick to the major suffering of a child who is in intensive care, no tear is overlooked by the St. Jude staff. Left: Small ones bear up with stiff lips and the escape of only an occasional tear.

To gain the confidence of a child who is to receive medication, it is often necessary to administer similar treatment to a favorite stuffed toy first (below).

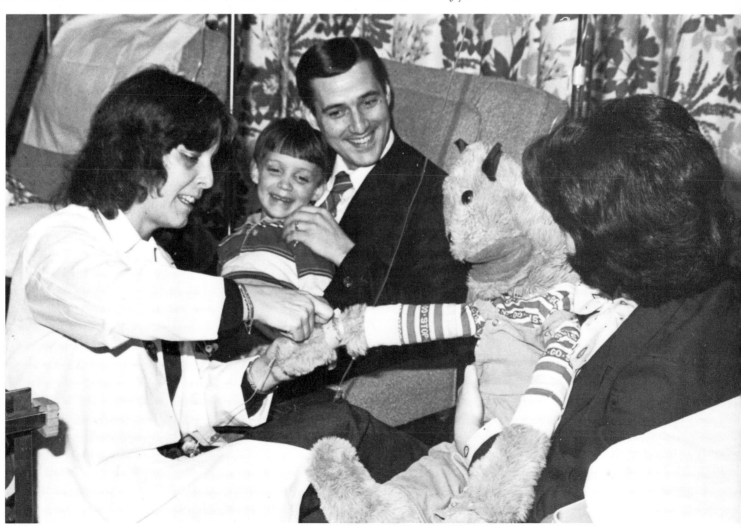

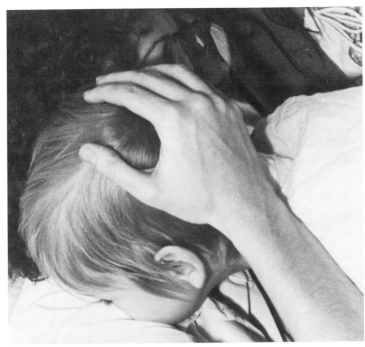

"When you work at St. Jude you cry a lot." The doctor who made this statement went on to add that he does his crying away from the children ... when a child hurts and when a child cries he loves it and encourages it.

Below: Inserting a needle brings tears but the same staff member also provides a big hug.

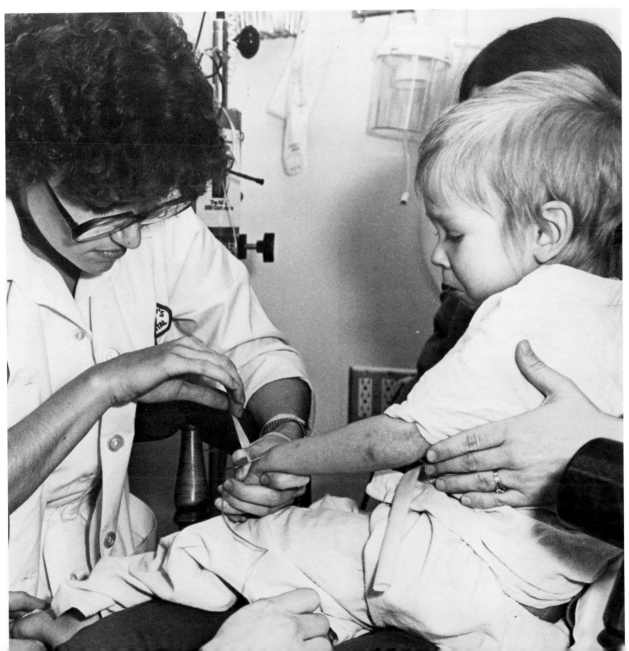

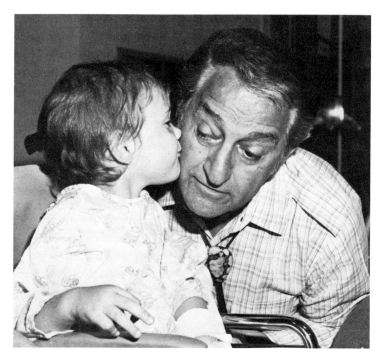

Right: When Danny is in the hospital he spends a lot of time with the children. Below: He holds a child close who is waiting for radiotherapy while he talks with other youngsters.

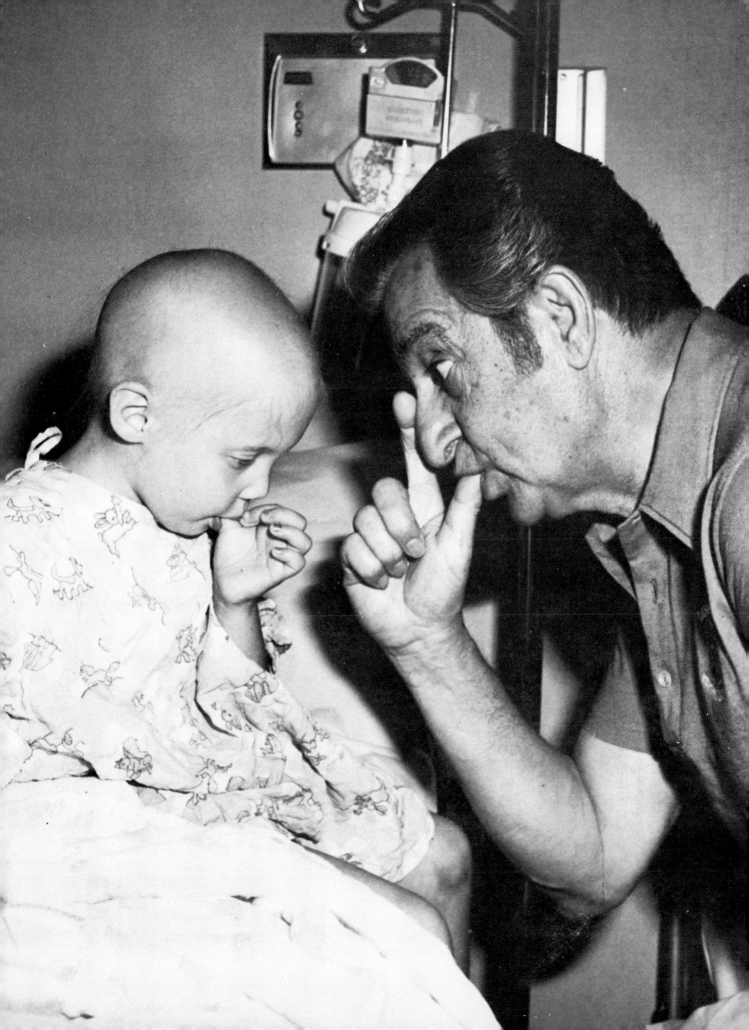

child crying because he didn't want the nurse to do the blood stick. Danny asked the nurse to give him a blood stick first. She did, and Danny Thomas cried, assuring the child, "See, I cry, too. It's all right to cry." The staff, and the founder, will stop at nothing to reassure a young patient!

Upstairs over the rotunda waiting room is the administration area. Dr. Mauer's office is here, as are the offices of Dr. Joseph Joseph Simone and R.L. Harrington, associate directors. The administrative offices, including admissions, grants management and public relations are also in this area as is the business office. And a truly unique business office it started out to be. True to the original intent of its founder, the hospital's business office had no accounts receivable ledger. But our ever-increasing bureaucracy soon made this impossible. When the hospital started accepting insurance payments on policies carried by the parents of the children who were being treated it became necessary to set up an accounts receivable system. But the original intent still remains — there is no direct cost to a child's family

for any part of the child's treatment at St. Jude Hospital.

A vital area on this floor is the medical records department. Charts are kept here on each child who has entered the hospital since the first one was admitted in March of 1962. About fifty or sixty new patients are admitted each month and each child has a detailed record from the first visit, complete with photographs, showing the child's progress and treatment. Some patient records are composed of several volumes. Kit Yatsula, head of the department, and her staff are almost as knowledgeable about the patients and their families as are the doctors who treat the children.

Adjacent to the medical records department is

Top: The Administration team at St. Jude Children's Hospital. From the left: Richard Harrington, Associate Director, Administration; Dr. Alvin M. Mauer, Director; Dr. Allan Granoff, Associate Director, Basic Research; Joseph V. Simone, Associate Director, Clinical Research.

the word processing center and across the hall is the medical library that contains over six thousand volumes of bound medical journals, over two hundred journal subscriptions and more than fifteen hundred book titles. It also provides services such as MEDLINE Computer Searches, several other computer database searches and manual bibliographic searches.

Comfortable sofas and tables and chairs are placed around the room for quiet study, and a small terrace opens to the outside where tables and chairs are provided for study and sunning, in combination, on nice Memphis days.

Downstairs, back of the rotunda lobby, a passageway leads to the cafeteria. The cafeteria was donated by the Hotel and Restaurant Employees and Bartenders International Union and they make regular contributions to maintain

---

Above: A comfortable corner of the Medical Library where current volumes of medical and scientific publications are shelved.

it. Here the director, the administrative staff, secretaries and volunteer workers join the doctors, researchers, lab technicians, nurses and the patients and their parents for noon meals and coffee breaks. There are no "reserved" signs on any area or any table in the room.

Young patients can find hamburgers done just the way they like them, a dieter can choose a salad and the daily hot lunch menu reads like a genuine Southern cookbook. Drinks and tempting goodies are also available for those who bring a lunch from home. And the conversation is always spirited, whether the subject is the hospital and their work, soccer or women's rights!

One wall of the cafeteria is all glass and looks out on a patio and passageway that connects the original Star of Hope with the new tower. The patio was built with a fund provided by American Airlines but, after the tower was completed, the only landscaping that had been done between the two buildings was the planting of grass to keep the soil from blowing away. All the money for the new building had been, of course, invested in construction and equipment.

One of the local garden clubs began a project to plant trees around the patio, but they soon saw that the project was bigger than one club could handle. They approached the Memphis and Shelby County Council of Garden Clubs and suggested that the Council might take on the project as a group endeavor.

Working with Larry Griffen, Memphis landscape architect, and Sandy Lewis, of the hospital administrative staff, a plan was drawn up that included an innovative playground for the children as well as the landscaping. The patio now contains eighteen cherry trees, six dogwoods and forty azalea bushes and provides a lovely oasis for the hospital employees and the patients they care for.

The corridor leading from the original building to the new tower has one glass wall overlooking the patio area. The opposite wall is lined with golden engraved memorial plaques. The architect had designed the main building to incorporate memorial tiles on the outside and inside lobby, but this space was rapidly filled. When the addition was built, the corridor wall seemed to be just right for the golden plaques, each commemorating a donation of a thousand dollars or more.

The corridor leads into a large lounge that is used by employees, patients, parents and visitors. Above the lounge on the second floor is a large reception lobby and the auditorium. The lobby is referred to as the Hall of Fame. It contains oil paintings of Ed Barry, Chairman of the Board of Governors, and Mike Tamer, the first director of ALSAC. Photos of other members of the Board of Governors and of ALSAC officers are on one wall.

Left: Medication continues even during lunch breaks. Above: Youngsters pick from a menu that appeals to them as well as to adults. In the cafeteria there are no special areas for patients, families, staff, or visiting V.I.P.'s . . . it's all one big happy family. Right: Trees of the patio are reflected in the glass of the building where some of the staff take their lunches out to sit on the wall and enjoy the sunshine.

There is a bust of Danny Thomas done by Margaret Huenergardt, the daughter of Colonel Sanders. And there is a painting done by Serena, a friend of Danny and Marlo Thomas. A plaque reminds visitors of the four million dollar cancer drive for St. Jude and the University of Tennessee Center for the Health Sciences and pays tribute to Sam Cooper and the men who helped him raise the funds.

And, at the far end of the room, a statue of St. Jude Thaddeus overlooks all the activity.

The auditorium is used for weekly faculty meetings. It is also used for employee meetings and for the Christmas skit that the staff presents each year. The referring physicians annual seminar is held in the auditorium as are a wide variety of other meetings and symposiums. On either side of the stage hang portraits of Danny Thomas and Dr. Donald Pinkel, donated to the hospital by the ladies of the Salon Circle.

The auditorium is dedicated to Abe Plough, founder of a Memphis Pharmaceutical company that merged in the early seventies to form Schering-Plough. Mr. Plough made the first research grant that St. Jude ever received, and

through the years he and the Plough Foundation have given generously to the hospital.

Adjacent to the auditorium, a corridor connects the second floor of the tower with the second floor of the original building. Along this corridor are the scientific editing offices and the volunteer services offices.

Over the last five years, staff members of St.

Above: The second floor lobby, adjacent to the auditorium. It is often used for receptions and, of course, for coffee breaks during conferences. Left: A portrait of Dr. Pinkel that hangs on the wall of the auditorium was presented to the hospital by the members of the Salon Circle. Shown here, left, Mrs. Nathan Bauman, president of the Salon Circle; Randy Jones; and Dr. Pinkel. The presentation was made in 1974 just prior to Dr. Pinkel's departure for a position at Milwaukee Children's Hospital.

Jude Hospital authored an average of two hundred professional papers a year, describing their research investigations and/or clinical findings. This work has appeared in such prestigious scientific publications as: Cancer, Cancer Research, Blood, Journal of Clinical Investigation, British Journal of Cancer, Review of Cancer Biology, Nature, Advanced Internal Medicine, Applied Therapeutics, Survey in Clinical Pediatrics and Journal of Laboratory Clinical Medicine, plus many others. The scientific editing staff provides invaluable help in the preparation of these articles and in the preparation of the annual scientific report.

The Volunteer Services staff was delighted to find what might prove to be a permanent home. Roberta Carder, director, recalls that in the years she has been with the hospital, her office has been moved from "closet" to "cubicle" and back as space was needed for ever-expanding research facilities.

Three floors of the tower are totally occupied by research laboratories. The third floor contains clinical therapeutics and pharmacology. Four is used for immunology and infectious disease research. And, the fifth floor, dedicated to Dr.

Donald Pinkel, is used for hematology and pathology offices and research.

Each research floor contains offices and laboratories plus a conference room. Every department holds weekly meetings and most meetings are open to any of the hospital staff. Each floor also has an incubator room, or a "warm" room. Certain experiments must be maintained at a constant warm temperature and these are conducted in the "warm" room. And, as there is a warm room, there is also a "cold" room. Each room is completely equipped with all necessary laboratory facilities and the temperature is controlled as needed for the experiments being conducted in the lab.

Each floor also contains an autoclave room that is equipped with machines similar to huge dishwashers that operate at an extremely high temperature. One person on each floor is solely responsible for the autoclave room. Every laboratory article, after it has been washed and sterilized, must also be either capped or topped with foil wrap to keep it sterile. All equipment for the entire floor is maintained in that floor's autoclave.

On each of the research floors are shower stalls

"Past experience has shown us that advances are least likely to come from the testing of known drugs. Rather they are to be found in the basic studies of cell growth and from the study of agents which stimulate, depress or alter metabolism in tissue cultures and in experimental animals.

We look to chemists, physicists, geneticists and virus and radio-isotope experts as well as to clinicians to solve the riddle of malignant disease. Progress in knowledge may be derived from studies in seemingly unrelated fields and in patients with diseases other than leukemia."

Right: A staff meeting in one of the conference rooms located on each floor. Center: An informal conference can take place almost anywhere. Opposite page: Working in a cold room demands proper attire. Bottom: Doctors check x-rays.

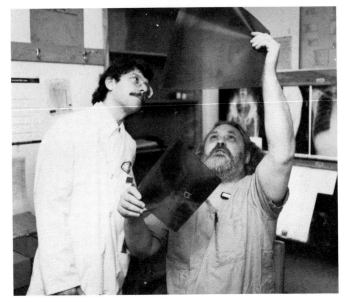

in the corridor. Should a researcher be working with a substance that splashes on him or gets into his eyes accidentally, he can rush into the corridor, wash out his eyes, or pull a lever that will release thirty gallons of water to wash over him instantly.

Researchers at St. Jude are particularly careful but accidents can happen and these stalls were planned in the design to be easily accessible to all the laboratories on the floor.

The sixth and seventh floors of the tower are the Inpatient floors at St. Jude. Every effort is made to keep from admitting children to the inpatient care area of the hospital. But when a child is admitted to St. Jude for treatment, it is often necessary for the youngster to be taken to the nursing floor for a period of a few days to as long as two weeks.

After all necessary testing is completed and the child is responding to the prescribed treatment, he or she is released to outpatient status and stays with parents at a local motel, returning to the hospital daily for treatment. Every effort is made to keep the child and parent together whenever possible.

The two patient floors are arranged to provide as much contact between parent and child as possible also. The two floors contain a total of forty-eight rooms, four of which are designated for intensive care. Almost never are the patient rooms all occupied — the average is twenty to twenty-two children daily.

The entry to the patient rooms is through a nursing station in the center of the area. On either side are the patient rooms. Each room is separated from the nursing area by a glass that allows the patients to be constantly monitored by the nurses on duty.

In this central nursing area there are no closets or cupboards since these are known to breed bacteria. It is important to maintain these two floors as bacteria-free as is humanly possible.

All supplies are on carts in the middle of the room. When the supplies are depleted, the carts are replenished by Central Supply. Linens, gowns, pajamas ... everything is out in the open.

In the patient rooms there are no air vents that can carry bacteria from room to room. The patient rooms are designed on an air pressure positive-two system where there is a constant controlled stream of purified air being pumped into the room. In this manner, the child breathes only purified air, greatly reducing the danger of infection.

Each room is also equipped with all monitoring equipment necessary to care for the child. No instruments or equipment are carried by the staff from room to room. There is also a pass-through for linens, trays and anything else that might go into or come out of the room.

There is a color television set that the child can control from the bedside. And, a private bath adjoins each room.

On the far side of the patient room is a parent room that is separated from the patient room by a glass. The entrance to this room is from an outside corridor. Each parent room is outfitted with a chair that makes into a bed and a black-and-white television set. The rooms are connected by a speaker system. The door from the bath into the parent room is kept locked. Parents enter the child's room only by going through the nursing area.

Unless a child has a secondary infection or the parent has an infection, one parent is allowed to be in the room with the child from nine in the morning until nine at night. It is believed that a parent's care and attention is extremely vital to the feeling of security the youngster needs when he or she is put "on the wing."

Visitors are also allowed in the parent room and, unlike most hospitals, there is no age restriction. A young patient's siblings and friends may visit, and even though they cannot be in the room with the child, they do talk

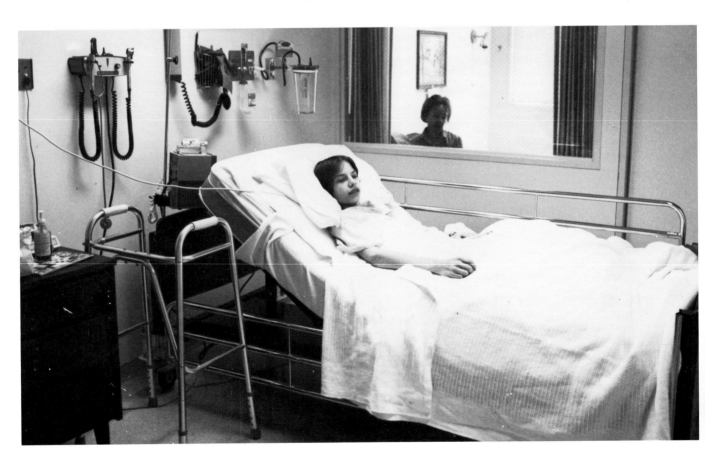

"If you can do something to deal with a child's suffering it's a very uplifting experience."

Opposite page: A young patient rests in her room, watched over by a parent in the adjoining room. Left: Access to parent rooms is through a corridor that runs along the outside of the tower. The view from the westside windows is relaxing as it overlooks the Mississippi River and the Tennessee-Arkansas bridge that so many of the young patients cross on their way to St. Jude. Lower: The hub of activity is the central nurse's station. From here, nurses on duty can observe activity in all the patient rooms.

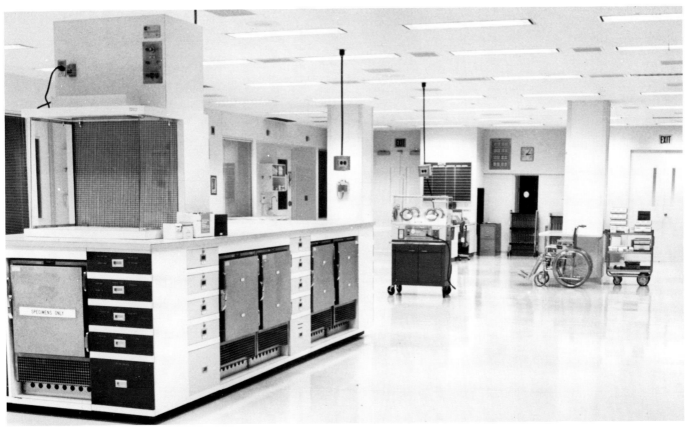

through the speaker system and are able to see one another. It makes being confined less frightening, both to the patient and the siblings.

If a youngster wants something unusual to eat, it is provided for him, unless a special diet precludes it. The nursing station contains a refrigerator and a microwave oven, and every effort is made to give the children the foods they want, when they want them. The chemotherapy treatment plays havoc with a child's appetite and, if the child expresses a desire for something special, even a Big Mac and French fries, it is provided. Special cold drinks are also kept as the child requests them.

The sixth floor of the hospital is dedicated to Frank Sinatra for the many benefits and help he has given the hospital through the years. The seventh floor is dedicated to Ray Kroc of McDonalds who donated a million dollars of stock to the hospital and whose restaurant crews are always available to help in telethons and special fund-raising projects.

Below: A mother relaxes in the parent room, secure in the knowledge that an intercom will bring her child's slightest request to her.

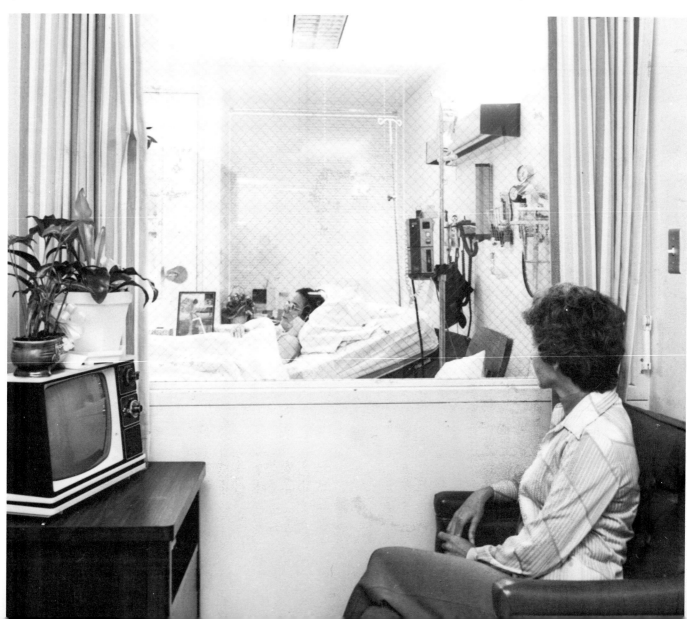

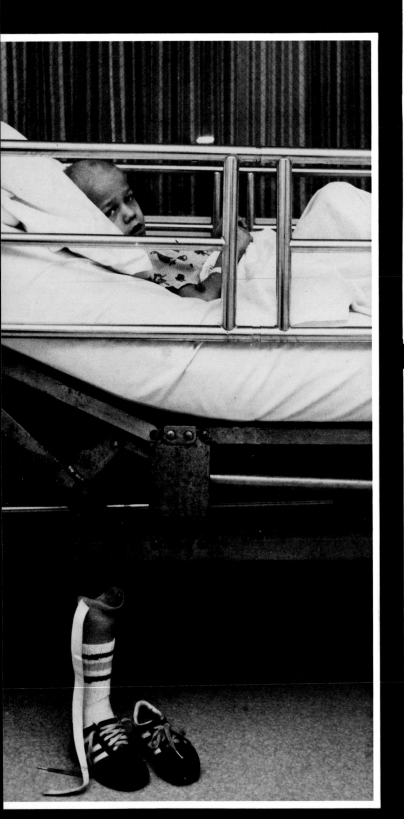
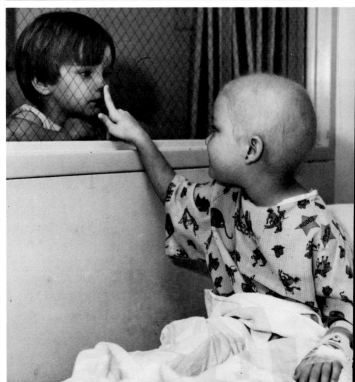
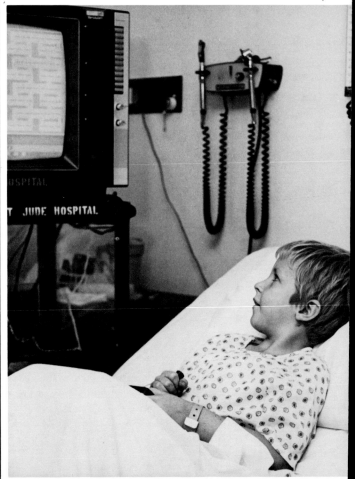

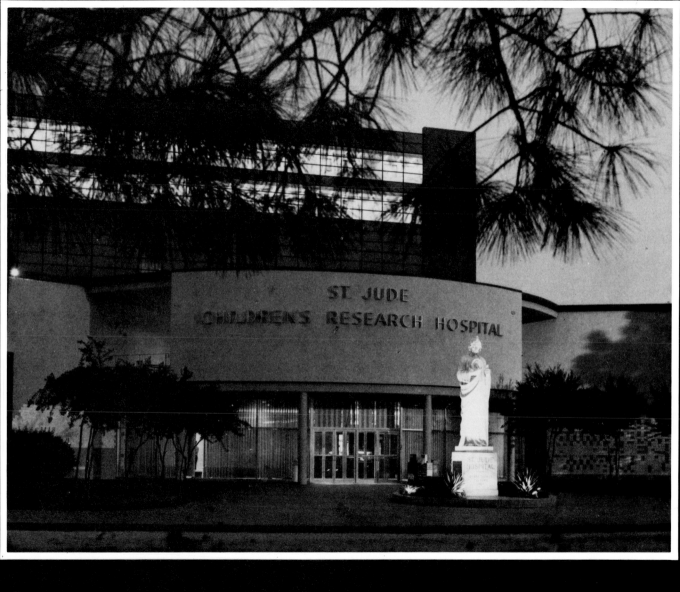

The dream of the people who work here would be to work themselves right out of their jobs, to be able to close the doors of St. Jude forever. But until that time comes, the lights will be burning throughout the night, every night, on the sixth and seventh floor at St. Jude Children's Research Hospital.

"Mike was the catalyst. Without him it would never have happened. He was the boss until the day he died."

ALSAC Reaches New Heights

As St. Jude Hospital continued to grow, to admit more patients, originate more studies, increase its professional staff, and seek more physical space, ALSAC grew side by side with it. The family structure that had formed the roots of the ALSAC organization was also to move toward a more structured corporate entity.

After Mike Tamer served the first year as volunteer national executive director and then succeeding years as a full-time paid executive director (his salary was minimal at his request), his tobacco and candy warehouse building became the first national offices of the ALSAC organization. It was staffed with more volunteer workers than paid staff members. Mike wanted it that way. And what he wanted, he made happen.

For years he ran an almost one-man operation. He was constantly approached by professional fund-raising organizations and he constantly turned them down. ALSAC would continue to be, under his direction, a volunteer organization.

Mike worked hard for ALSAC and St. Jude Hospital — almost two decades of his life were dedicated to it. Few men knew that Mike Tamer was a self-made man, that he had very little formal education. He was small of stature but was a giant among men. He could talk to a crowd — some say he shouted rather than talked — and strike that nerve in each person that would make him want to give to support this cause that this man believed in so very much.

Danny recalls, "He would quit every year . . . he was tired. I'd say, 'Mike, we've come this far.' And he'd say, 'O.K., one more year'. The next year I would say I was tired and he would remind me, 'Danny, we've come this far . . .' and he would repeat my speech of the year before word for word."

Right: The first ALSAC National Executive Office at 611 Massachusetts Avenue in Indianapolis, Indiana. The building had previously housed Mike Tamer's Candy and Tobacco Company. Center: Tamer, standing at the left, meets with the ALSAC Executive Board in the early days and (lower) discusses fund-raising strategy with Joseph S. Ayoub, Minor George, Victor Swyden and Mrs. Mitchell B. Forzley.

Mike Tamer addresses early ALSAC convention. From left, then Executive Vice President Bud Rashid, Tamer, Danny Thomas, Executive Secretary La Vonne Rashid.

Mike delighted in recalling that "this man Thomas" had assured him in 1957 that the hospital was going to cost a million dollars to build and three hundred thousand dollars a year to maintain. He would follow this statement with, "I knew I shouldn't have trusted that Thomas because it cost two million to build and a million a year to maintain — at the start — and from then on I was stuck."

When there were money problems, Danny and Mike worried them through together. They would attend a meeting of the Board of Governors where the members would decide that there really was not money available for a new piece of equipment that was needed by the doctors and researchers at the hospital.

But Danny and Mike knew, as did the Board members, that the equipment was needed. Danny recalls that they would go back to Mike's hotel room after the meeting and sit and talk about it. Just when Danny thought they might be going to bed, Mike would light a fresh cigar, and Danny knew they were in for a long session. But when the wee small hours of the morning rolled around and they finally did retire, Mike had found a way for the doctors to have the equipment that was needed.

But Mike Tamer was not only a dreamer and an idealist — he was also a realist. As the move into the decade of the seventies began, so also began Mike Tamer's move into a more structured organization for ALSAC.

In the beginning years he had called upon his and Danny's people of Syrian/Lebanese ancestry to invest time, talents and money in a volunteer effort for St. Jude Hospital. This a small dedicated group had done willingly and, often, at great personal sacrifice.

Members of this group served on the hospital Board of Governors, and were regional directors or city directors of the ALSAC volunteer chapters. All expenses they incurred, all travel and lodging costs were borne by each individual member personally. More often than not husband and wife, plus members of their family, were involved in working long hours for the hospital. During the decade of the sixties more than one had either lost, or come close to losing,

---

"They make men like Mike Tamer but they don't make many of them. They have a way of handling things and appealing to people."

his business because of devotion to ALSAC, St. Jude Hospital and Mike Tamer and Danny Thomas personally.

But as the needs for the hospital continued to grow and increase the yearly operational costs to ALSAC, Mike Tamer saw the need to structure an organization that would carry some paid full-time staff members. This was, in no way, to diminish the dedicated work of the volunteers — it would augment it.

The first regional office of ALSAC was set up in Memphis with Al Toler as southern regional director. His offices were located in an area on the second floor of the hospital building and Al settled in to organize ALSAC's fund raising efforts in the southern states, the area that had sent more children as patients to St. Jude in the 1960's than any other.

In 1973, Mike Tamer transferred Al Toler to Indianapolis as his assistant. One of the first items on his agenda was to review all the offices that were staffed with part time volunteers. As a result of his study, many of these were closed and five full-time offices were set up with five full-time regional directors.

Standards were established for the operation of the fifty or sixty certified chapters that dotted the country. Al Toler recalls a lot of "trial and error" in the organization of these field offices and their operation as related to the volunteers who were still the backbone of the ALSAC organization.

During these early 1970 years the new addition was under construction and more and more monies would be needed to fund its operation. There was also a decrease in the percentage of operating costs covered by federal grants. Added strain was put on ALSAC during these days, but there was only one year in that period that ALSAC did not raise as much money as was needed for the operation of the hospital. The goal, of course, was to build and maintain a fund balance that would act as a cushion against the yearly operating expenditures.

On November 13, 1974, Mike Tamer died at the age of 70. He had dedicated seventeen years — almost two decades of his life — to St. Jude Children's Research Hospital. He had sought no honors, no credit for this effort. He had created an organization that grew from nothing into one of the most important charities in America.

No one was more surprised than he the day that Danny took him out the front door of the hospital, down the drive, where he unveiled a plaque at the entrance to the driveway. It is more than fitting that, since that day, each child who arrives for life-giving treatment at St. Jude Children's Research Hospital enters the hospital compound by way of M. F. Tamer Drive.

And, in remembering Mike Tamer, one is reminded of the words of Kahlil Gibran in *The Prophet*, "You give but little when you give of your possessions. It is when you give of yourself that you truly give."

Mike Tamer truly gave his life for this cause which he so deeply believed in.

Left: Danny surprised Mike Tamer the day they dedicated the M. F. Tamer Drive, the entrance to St. Jude Hospital. Lower: The fun days and the serious days of ALSAC. Donating blood just after the hospital opened with a little help from his friends (left to right) George Gattas, Joe Gattas and Dr. Floyd Nassif.

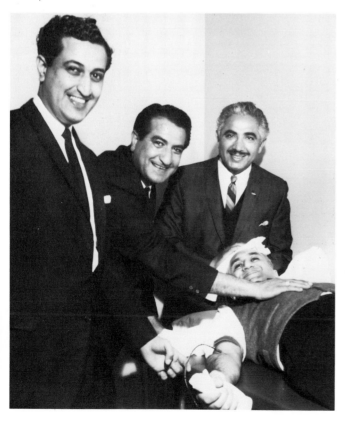

Reeling from Mike Tamer's death, the ALSAC organization formed an executive committee, headed by Richard Shadyac, an attorney from Virginia, to supervise the day to day operation of the office. A search began for a new executive director.

Fred P. Gattas, a Memphis resident who had been involved with St. Jude from its very beginning, was appointed as interim national executive director. As an unpaid volunteer, he took a six month leave of absence from his catalog showroom business in Memphis to move to Indianapolis to head ALSAC.

Gattas accepted the responsibility with two objectives firmly in mind. One was to move the ALSAC national offices to Memphis and the other was to build a building to house the staff of these offices. He met with a great deal of opposition from other members of the ALSAC organization.

There were those who wanted the office located in Washington, D.C. and others who preferred Boston or a variety of other cities. But, after much heated debate, the office was moved to Memphis, and Fred P. Gattas was asked by the Board of Governors to serve an additional six months. A selection had been made for the position, but the nominee would not be available for another six months.

In July of 1976, Baddia J. Rashid retired from his position as Director of Operations of the Antitrust Division of the Justice Department and took over the helm of ALSAC. He had been actively involved with ALSAC since 1957.

And the building that was to house the ALSAC offices in Memphis was completed and was only a stone's throw from the hospital.

Bud Rashid was the first to acknowledge that many challenges lay ahead. Mike Tamer's personal charisma had served well in keeping the ALSAC volunteers out working for St. Jude Hospital in those earlier days. Many stated that the only reason they stayed involved as long as they did was because of Mike.

But the days when Mike could tell volunteer chapters that the deficit in one year's income would be added to their goal for the next year were obviously gone. Only Mike Tamer was able to make that threat . . . and make it work. But, even he had determined that those days were passing and he had been working toward a much more structured organization.

One of Bud Rashid's first goals was to increase

Above: Fred P. Gattas, interim executive director of ALSAC following Mike Tamer's death, looks into a research project at St. Jude and (below) he and Dr. Mauer welcome Baddia J. Rashid to his new office in the ALSAC building that had recently been completed in Memphis.

the fund balance. By imposing centralized accounting procedures, placing tighter controls on expenses and by establishing new fund-raising guidelines this has been accomplished.

Since money raised in one year is normally used for the hospital's expenses the following year, if the fund-raising goal for that year is not reached, the difference must be taken from the next year's funds. In 1976 the fund balance was increased by $137,926 and each year since has seen even much greater increases, passing in excess of thirteen million dollars by 1982. Rashid's and the Board of Directors' goal is to have a full year's operating expenses as a reserve fund balance.

Bud Rashid's next step was to analyze, reorganize and expand the professional staff to provide an expansion of fund-raising efforts to all parts of the United States. There were some areas in the country where the general public knew little about the hospital other than occasionally seeing Danny talk about his hospital on television shows. Entire sections of the country were not being given a chance to contribute on a continuing basis.

In early 1977, the Board of Directors approved Bud Rashid's plan. Following an intensive search, William J. Kirwen was appointed Director of Development. His assignment was easy to say: take charge of all fund-raising activities of the thousands of volunteer groups across the country and of the staff in the Memphis office.

He was to then increase the income from these sources to meet the hospital's projected needs.

"I think I looked as closely at the hospital and ALSAC as they looked at me, and I knew it wouldn't be easy," Kirwen observed. "But, after seeing St. Jude, the hospital, I knew that St. Jude, the saint, was behind us, and there was no way we could fail."

Within two months, a new program was being tested that would reach people living in smaller communities. Titled the Community Development Program, it relied on telephone power, support material and incentives to organize and conduct a once-a-year bike ride or door-to-door campaign. The first 1977 pilot brought in $77,000. Since then the CDP has grown into a four million dollar a year program that reaches people in more than ten thousand small communities with the story of St. Jude Hospital.

Math-A-Thon was tried as a pilot program in the Mid-Atlantic Region in 1978, and has since expanded into all eleven regions. Fran Madrid, creator of the program, says of it, "Unlike most fund-raising projects, Math-A-Thon gives its participants something valuable in return. Each participant gets both a social inter-reaction with the outside world by asking for support, but they also supplement and improve their math skills by solving the problems we provide." In the 1981-1982 school year, this program was conducted in 5,577 schools and raised four and a half million dollars for the hospital.

Executive staff of ALSAC, 1982. From left: Dennis Morlok, Bud Rashid, Danny Thomas, Bill Kirwen, Dave McKee.

Danny Thomas checks ALSAC's computer operation. From left, Paul Parham, Danny, Doug Marchant, Marti Beasley, Bud Rashid, and Dennis Morlok.

In early 1982, these programs were consolidated under a new CDP Department charged with increasing proven programs and developing new ones along similar lines.

Rashid and Kirwen also began filling in the gaps in ALSAC's regional organization. The Southeast Regional office in Atlanta opened in December 1977, followed closely by the Mid-Atlantic Region in Washington, D.C. and the Southwestern Region in Austin, Texas. By 1978, ALSAC had acquired the leadership necessary in its regional offices to effect orderly and efficient expansion. New programs and changes in old ones could be tested in order to build on former successes.

Today, regional offices in ten cities coordinate activities in all areas of the country, including Alaska, Hawaii, and our island territories.

In the early days of ALSAC Mike Tamer called upon a friend who had been doing the printing for his wholesale business. Robert J. O'Brian was a printer with little or no experience in direct mail. Mike Tamer was a director of a charity

with little or no experience in direct mail. They pooled their resources and a great partnership developed that was to last until Mike's death. Bob O'Brian says today that Mike Tamer was like a father to him and if "any man can love another man, then surely I loved Mike Tamer."

Together they set up a mailing program — the first pieces going to Arabic-speaking mailing lists. In the early appeals they invited people to become Founding Fathers of St. Jude Hospital. Contribution of a hundred dollars would be a founder; five hundred dollars was the price of a silver founder; and a thousand guaranteed the contributor a gold founding father status.

These mailings continued until 1961 when a direct mail program was set up with Bob O'Brian's firm putting up the front money of $275,000 to fund it for the first year or two. His firm was to write the copy, do the layouts and artwork, plus the printing. They would maintain mailing lists, put the appeals in the mail, receive the replies, acknowledge them, bank and keep records of the money received and forward regular checks to ALSAC.

The first mailing was 25,000 pieces. And, the experiments that Mike and Bob made in direct mail paid off. Within two years ALSAC had returned the seed money and a large number of contributions were pouring in regularly.

In July of 1969 a newsletter originated from the direct mail program that went to a group of major contributors to keep them apprised of what was happening at the hospital and at ALSAC.

In 1972 they started the sweepstakes. The first sweepstakes drawing was from a barrel with a capacity of 300,000 stubs. The last drawing that was held in Indianapolis was from a barrel with a capacity of eight million stubs.

When the Board decided in 1981 to transfer the direct mail program from O'Brian's firm in Indianapolis to a newly formed Department of Direct Mail Appeals in the Memphis ALSAC office, the mailings for the previous year had topped fifty million pieces. The last year's receipts from the direct mail program had been in excess of twelve million dollars. And more than two million active donor names were turned over to the national office.

That was not bad for two men, Bob O'Brian and Mike Tamer, who had been "experimenting" with direct mail to raise money for the hospital! For many years the direct mail program was the single largest source of revenue for the hospital. And by the end of the first year, the Mail Appeals Department had made it even more so while reducing the cost by almost half. Modern direct mail techniques, elimination of the sweepstakes and reduction of prospect mailing brought in $10-2-million at a cost of only $2.6-million.

By 1978, the building that Fred P. Gattas had built to house the national ALSAC offices was filled to capacity and, in fact, was overflowing. The supply storeroom had been converted to offices and the conference room was being used to assemble volunteer kits for the various programs. Fred P. Gattas once again stepped in and provided temporary storage space in his downtown warehouse for tons of material, but it was obvious to all that more space was needed.

"St. Jude seemed to be watching again," Bill Kirwen recalls. "Just as we needed it, one of our suppliers, a printing firm across the street, told us they were moving. We were able to lease this building, giving us room for expansion."

Much of this material is produced by three people who comprise the Communications Department, which also produces and distributes national public service announcements for radio, television and magazines several times each year. Run by the media free of charge as a public service contribution these announcements keep St. Jude Hospital before the public through the year.

This department has also produced award-winning films about the hospital as well as the quarterly *ALSAC News* newspaper, brochures and pamphlets and the combined annual report of the hospital and ALSAC. It also provides expert creative advice, design and production service for other ALSAC departments, being responsible for all materials from a small number of forms for a pilot program to the eight million bike ride sponsor forms that were used this year by volunteers in their campaigns.

The communications staff also fills in where needed — directing surveys, developing and directing the first direct mail campaign after the program was moved to Memphis, editing and supervising production of the first five years' telethon tapes — thus providing an important link between all other departments, the volunteers, the public and the hospital.

Prior to 1961, ALSAC had staged a variety of events in towns and cities across the nation to raise money for the hospital. One of the first coordinated events was the placing of coin canisters in retail establishments. Coins played an important part in fund-raising for St. Jude.

When the hospital was dedicated, Mrs. H.H. Neumann of Ashland, Oregon sent Danny a picture of her son and coins he had collected for the hospital. The first wishing well report to come into the ALSAC offices was a contribution in 1959 from a well in Boukair's Seesweets Shop in Cleveland, Ohio. Through the years money continued to flow into the offices from fountain and wishing wells across the country. In 1977, the manager of the Hungry Fisherman restaurant in Memphis cleaned out his fountain and put coins in a wheelbarrow for delivery to the hospital. The $552.60 was perhaps, at that time, the largest amount ever recorded from a wishing well or fountain.

In the early days of the hospital, Danny would talk about the importance of coins, as well as dollars. "One dollar — even a dime — buys

Danny Thomas checks the new ALSAC National Executive Office building in Memphis, the third building within a twenty year period of time.

something. But when you put all the dimes and dollars together, their power for good is simply massive."

Among the early fund-raisers for St. Jude were children who suffered from serious illness themselves. In the fall of 1959, eight-year old Marlene Winter, of Milwaukee, Wisconsin — a victim of rheumatic fever — offered five puppies for sale with the proceeds going to charity. She explained that half would go to the Heart Fund and half to Danny Thomas' leukemia fund. The net result for St. Jude was eight dollars, pennies from the heart.

In this group of youngsters who raised pennies for St. Jude, Ann Hill, of Ashland, Mississippi, stands far in front though she was never able to stand during the twenty-five years of her life. Ann had a rare disease that had confined her to a wheel chair from infancy. But, from that wheel chair, when she was eleven years old, Ann sold lemonade to raise $1,108.00 to give Danny when the hospital opened. And, at that time, the population of Ashland was 319!

For her dedication through the years, Ann Hill was named volunteer chairman of the entire state of Mississippi and she coordinated all fund raising activities in her state for St. Jude. Ann continued to work with teen marches and other events and, at her death in the fall of 1970, ALSAC announced that she had helped raise almost $150,000 for the hospital. She knew that her illness was not one that would be studied at St. Jude but she also knew what it meant for a child to suffer. She was truly the "Spirit of ALSAC" in its formative years.

But large contributions are also needed to help the hospital in its battle against catastrophic diseases. Sometimes these come in very strange ways. One December in 1977, a young, casually dressed couple walked into the hospital and said that they would like to talk to someone about making a donation. Sandy Lewis, executive secretary of the Board of Governors and an administrative assistant in the hospital, met with them in her office. They handed her nine

Left: Bernard Giovanni, owner of Bernard's Cocktail Lounge in Detroit, empties cannister into bag held by George Simon, Ethel Horste and Toby David. Below: Susan and Nancy Haddad of Allentown, Pennsylvania sell lemonade to neighbor Roger Miller. Left Bottom: Ann Hill is presented an Outstanding Woman of ALSAC award by Danny Thomas.

envelopes. Seven were marked with the number "1" and two were marked with the number "2".

The young man who was in his 20's told her that the number designated the number of thousands of dollars in each envelope. Not certain that it was a hoax, but knowing that there was nothing to lose in accepting the envelopes, Sandy took them without opening them.

She took the young couple back down into the lobby where they bought two St. Jude medals from the gift shop. She offered them a tour of the hospital but they told her that they had to return to the airport to catch their flight.

After thanking them again and bidding them goodbye, Sandy returned to her office where she opened the envelopes. The markings were indeed correct. There were five hundred and fifty twenty dollar bills . . . a total of $11,000. "They said that St. Jude had blessed them with some favors," Sandy recalls. They left without a receipt or without naming a person in whose name the money was given — a truly anonymous donation!

But St. Jude Hospital cannot rely on occasional windfalls of this type. ALSAC has to solicit big money . . . from foundations, corporations, planned giving, wills and large individual bequests. A Planned Giving Department was added in 1978 and in 1981, a Department for Corporate and Foundation Relations became part of the national offices. The members of the staff are specialists in helping individuals, foundations, and corporations donate large sums while also obtaining the best possible tax advantage in each case.

In 1962, just as the hospital opened its doors, Danny Thomas received a letter from a lady in Florida. It read:

Dear Danny Thomas,
  I am one of your (older) fans — but that isn't what I'm writing for. I'm interested in your hospital plan — I'm making my will — I don't have very much but I'd like to have what little I have left go to the most good for those who need it.
  I talked with Dr. Ronau of St. Anthony's Hospital here and I asked him about you. He was going to suggest it.
  Please mail me all the information I need to put in my will. Thank you in advance.
                                   I am,
                                   Sincerely,
                                   Marie J. Fisk
                                   St. Petersburg, Florida

Today the Planned Giving Department has literature available for such requests. And Danny's people are available to talk with anyone who is interested in making a donation of this type.

A great milestone in the history of ALSAC was the introduction of the Teenagers March. These were the brainchild of still another business associate of Mike Tamer. Rich White and his father had an advertising specialty business in Indianapolis. Mike called one day, using the yellow pages, and asked to see some materials for fund-raising. That contact began an association that was to last from 1958 through 1973.

Rich designed and developed the first coin canisters that were sent out all over the country to be placed in retail establishments to collect money for the hospital. After a period of working with Mike on fund-raising ideas, Mike asked him if he would work with ALSAC as a semi-professional fund raiser. He joined the staff on a part-time basis.

One day while driving from one appointment to another he had the brainstorm that was the origin of the teenage marches. He felt that teens were basically very good and they only needed a challenge to rise to great heights. And, what more challenge could there be than raising funds for a children's hospital — kids helping kids.

Left: Rich White, originator of the Teen Marches. Right: Mrs. M. F. Tamer assists Ethel Horste and other Detroit volunteers in counting the funds from their first Teen March in 1964. The total was a staggering $110,000!

Working with local radio stations in Indianapolis he recruited teens who marched one Sunday afternoon in September of 1961 for Danny Thomas and St. Jude Hospital. They collected $17,000 and the Teen Marches were launched.

Mike asked Rich to leave his business and work full time with ALSAC organizing the Teen Marches. He did, visiting seventy-five cities the first year. The idea of the Proud Beggars caught hold with all the local chapters and they moved swiftly to organize their own areas. All materials were provided by the national office and coordinated by local groups.

Complex systems were set up for the marches and in most areas were highly structured and involved thousands of teens. Competition was keen between cities and the national conventions always brought out this spirit in announcing the results of the past year's marches. For many years Detroit and Cleveland vied for top honors. Detroit took the lead in 1965 and stayed there for eight years.

MILAN, ITALY
May 18, 1962

A transatlantic phone call from the Chicago Chapter of A.L.S.A.C. (Aiding Leukemia Stricken American Children) reached me in Milan, Italy during our European trip.

They told me of the fabulous job that was done by you Teen-Agers in the Greater Chicago area and the many other towns and cities in Illinois that took part in our "Teen-Age March Against Leukemia."

You raised over $22,000.00 to help support the Danny Thomas, St. Jude Research Hospital and at the time of this writing Kewanee and Rock Island were still to hold their "March".

I wonder if you young men and women know just what this meant to me. First I see a dream of some 25 years become reality with the opening of our new free hospital for victims of Leukemia, and then you young folks come crashing through with this magnificent and unselfish effort on our behalf.

It is fitting that you young people gave this evidence of your devotion to our cause, for, as you know this dread killer strikes mostly among the very young, the very helpless, the very blameless.

To all of you - to your mothers and fathers - to my own people of Lebanese and Syrian descent - to the newspapers, television, radio, and all others of every race, color and creed who helped in the promotion and execution of this wondrous program, my heartfelt thanks.

But to you young folks, who did the actual job I say God bless you from my heart.

The future of our country is in safe hands.

My love and affection goes out to you in full measure.

                              Gratefully,

                              Danny Thomas

                              Danny Thomas

Opposite page: A thank you letter from Danny Thomas to the Teens who marched in Illinois in 1962 for St. Jude Hospital. Top: Bobby Rydell, national chairman, with teens in Greenville, Pennsylvania. Above: Cleveland ALSAC teams plan a 1964 march. Left: Danny with teens at the 1964 ALSAC convention.

Danny was to say, "Give the teenagers a good cause to rally around and they'll break their backs for you."

But times change, and with them, children's activities. By the 1970's more and more children owned bicycles. The idea of bike rides for St. Jude was born in a kitchen in Seymour, Indiana. The idea was Mrs. Judy Lester's and in January of 1971 she proposed a national bike ride sponsored by ESA International of which she was a member. That sparked a series of bike rides and bike-a-thons across the country that have lasted throughout one decade and entered into another.

Local communities go all-out in their bike-a-thon efforts. In Manson, Iowa members of the community (2,200 strong) supported thirty-five bike riders with contributions totalling $1,126.20. This would not be unique except that it was done less than a year after the town was devastated by a tornado and while the town was still being rebuilt.

A small farming community of Lyford-Sebastian, Texas raised $5,040.33 with a bike ride. One young man, only fourteen years old, rode sixty miles and collected $1,373.00 from forty-nine sponsors.

And Fort Wayne, Indiana's fifth annual bike ride broke all their previous records when they raised $32,502.00. That was $8,000 more than the previous year. Several St. Jude patients rode in the 1980 ride as did two nurses from the St. Jude staff in Memphis.

Left: Riders register for Community Development Program bike ride. Top: Dan Kuykendall, Congressman from district where St. Jude Hospital is located checks the route with two bikers in Memphis. Above: Bike rides attract variety. Danny Jacques rode 35 miles for St. Jude on his 8-foot unicycle. Opposite page: Lisa Gillentine, St. Jude poster child for 1978-79 Wheels For Life bike rides.

In the 1980's the bike-a-thons are still being held but with the increased interest in running many local groups are now sponsoring "Run for St. Jude" events. And, in 1981 eighteen Sigma Nu fraternity brothers jogged non-stop the 300 miles from Hattiesburg, Mississippi to St. Jude Hospital. Their relay raised $6,000 for the hospital.

Many other ideas are used by local communities to raise funds for St. Jude. Teenagers today still have car washes to raise money. But their effort has also been supplemented in Memphis by a firm that operates a chain of car washes. In its first car wash for St. Jude in June of 1980 it raised more than $22,000 for St. Jude. During the month more than 40,000 cars were washed with fifty cents each being donated to the hospital. The company planned to make it an

Opposite page: Young bike rider displays his cause. The youngster is Scott Vogel, son of St. Jude Hospital Board's executive secretary Sandy Vogel Lewis. Scott solicited pledges from some of the Board of Directors for his ride in 1975. Above: The High Wheelers from Memphis Naval Air Station rode fifty miles on these bikes. Right: Norfolk, Virginia runners set off on marathon for St. Jude.

annual affair — but they also gave credit where it was due — to the teenagers who began car washing for a cause!

A few years ago youngsters started collecting aluminum cans, recycling them and donating the money to St. Jude. In Memphis many people take their cans to Dixie Recycling Company and request that the money that would be paid them be paid to St. Jude. Some nurses at the hospital collect a large number of cans and bring them in requesting that the money be sent to the hospital.

In addition, since the company began its recycling effort in 1978, it has paid St. Jude one cent for each pound of cans it buys. This is in addition to the monies paid the person who brings in the cans. Also in Memphis the distributor of Miller Beer, Premium Brands, Inc., co-sponsored with Miller Brewing Company, a contest to encourage college students to pick up and recycle Miller cans. The firm buys the cans for fifteen cents a pound and sells them to the recycling company for thirty cents a pound, donating the entire thirty cents to St. Jude. Recycling is paying off for St. Jude youngsters.

But the big checks that come in from the large companies are often overshadowed by smaller checks sent in by a single person. Mel Poole of Sparks, Nevada is in his seventies and is retired.

He heard on a local radio station about a little girl from Sparks who was being treated at St. Jude and he began collecting cans and sending the money to the hospital. For the past nine years he has worked at this effort from four to six hours a day, rain or shine, and sends St. Jude checks that sometimes run to over $200.00 a month.

In some areas the children organize "Jello Jumps" and the adults are equally as innovative. One group has a classic car auction that raises thousands of dollars for the hospital.

The Decatur County Coon Hunters Association combines sport with charity in its annual "World's Largest Coon Hunt for St. Jude" where over $30,000 is raised in one effort. Coon hunters from all over the country enter their dogs in this event where no raccoons are killed and guns are forbidden. Contests are held for the hunters and their dogs and everyone gets into the act by staging auctions, radiothons, country music entertainment and food booths manned by local Jaycees and Jayceettes.

There are also the glamour events that are staged for the benefit of the hospital. The Inspiration Ball was founded by the City Director of the Greater Detroit Chapter of ALSAC, Ethel

Copy of article appearing in the ALSAC News in 1981

Mel Poole of Sparks, Nevada is 73 years old and retired. For the past nine years he has been collecting aluminum cans and sending the money he gets from having them recycled to St. Jude.

He heard on the radio about a little girl from Sparks who was being treated at St. Jude and began to collect the cans. It was slow at first, taking several months to collect enough to send in a $10 donation.

Then he built a cart and worked 4-6 hours every day, rain or shine. Now he sends St. Jude checks of sometimes $200 a month. He figures he has sent over $1500 to St. Jude just from collecting aluminum cans.

Mr. Poole's only wish for his outstanding effort was to talk to Danny Thomas, and his wish was granted recently when Danny was performing in Las Vegas.

Mel Poole of Sparks, NV and his cart for collecting aluminum cans for SJ.

Bekolay Horste, a member of the original Board of Governors of St. Jude Hospital and still an active member. She founded the ball in honor of her daughter, Jacquie, who fought illness courageously and lived. The ball is an annual event which has raised over $630,000 to date.

In Miami, Florida, the Miracle Ball was first held in 1961. The twentieth anniversary ball was held in 1981 and raised $200,000 for the hospital. Anthony Abraham and George Elias, both members of the Board of Governors, are the originators of this ball which is held in the Fountainbleau Hotel and each year brings a top name entertainer to the event.

In New York each summer a gala is staged by the National Catalog and Jewelry Industry to honor St. Jude Hospital and B'nai B'rith Youth Services. Monies raised are divided equally between the two organizations. The 1981 event brought Danny Thomas and his entire night club act to New York to help raise $170,000 for the hospital.

John Grisanti, noted Memphis restaurateur, is an ardent supporter of St. Jude Hospital. He

hospital . . . the pharmacology division of St. Jude is dedicated to her.

But Rose Marie Thomas was not to rest on her laurels. The following year she threw what came to be known as a "million dollar bash." On July 11, 1980 she, along with two thousands friends and admirers of Frank Sinatra, gathered at the Century Plaza Hotel in Beverly Hills to help Frank and Barbara Sinatra celebrate their fourth wedding anniversary.

The gala was billed "Sinatra Sings: A Night in Italy." Frank did sing and Danny presented him with a plaque of the logo of St. Jude Hospital aptly inscribed "to the legend and the man." That night a million dollars was raised in one single event for St. Jude! Rose Marie's goal had been half a million!

made history at an auction of rare old wines when he bid the highest price ever paid for a single bottle of wine. He returned to Memphis with the wine and uncorked it at a wine-tasting party held to benefit the hospital. A gourmet dinner and a sip of wine, at $1400 per person, brought $45,000 to the hospital.

In 1980, he broke his previous record by paying $31,000 for a 158-year old bottle of Chateau Lafite. Nine Memphis businessmen, along with Big John, each contributed $3,000 to purchase the wine at the auction. Two hundred people paid two hundred dollars each for the privilege of attending a wine-tasting gala where lots were drawn to see who would be among the few who would actually sip a portion of the rare wine. Big John raised $53,000 from this event. On both occasions the wine was pronounced to be "perfect."

And, on the West Coast in Los Angeles, a person who has been very close to Danny Thomas and St. Jude Hospital for many years was to set a record in 1979. Rose Marie Thomas, Danny's wife and partner, produced and directed the most successful fundraising dinner in the history of ALSAC.

Almost 1500 people — film personalities, sports stars, corporate executives, government officials — all were to contribute a minimum of $125.00 each. More than a hundred checks and reservations were returned for lack of space. Included in contributions that night was a check for $100,000 from singer Phyllis McGuire and Mike Davis. It was her third such donation to the

There are entire communities that have been involved with St. Jude Hospital for years. Paul lived in Albany, Georgia and when he was seven years old, in 1966, he was referred to St. Jude. His family and friends were told that he would not live more than six weeks. Paul and his family still live in Albany and his neighbors and family are thankful to St. Jude Hospital.

Each year, under the continuous leadership of Joe Farris, the residents of Albany, along with their neighbors from the communities of Pelham and Douglas, hold road blocks, door-to-door campaigns, sell peanuts, have car washes and a dance-a-thon to raise money for their yearly contribution. They started working for the hospital three years before it opened and for many years the members of the community came to St. Jude by the busload to bring "Christmas in July" to children who might not live to see it in December.

Now there is no need for an early Christmas, but the group still arrives in Memphis each summer to bring toys and the monies they have collected during the year. It's now called the "July Jubilee" and in one year alone these small communities of that rural Georgia area will bring in as much as $6,000 in cash and 2,000 toys to the hospital.

Above: John Grisanti of Memphis presents check to Danny Thomas from his wine-tasting bash. Opposite page top: Danny and Rose Marie Thomas present a plaque to Frank and Barbara Sinatra in Beverly Hills in 1980.

The people do it with thanksgiving — several of the children in their community are among the "miracle" children of St. Jude Hospital. One of the latest of these is Josh. Josh has been a patient of St. Jude since he was eighteen months old. After his illness was diagnosed, his father lost his job in Albany and the doctors and staff at St. Jude helped him to relocate in Memphis.

After their arrival in Memphis, Josh's mother was diagnosed as having breast cancer, and, again, the St. Jude staff rallied to the family's side to arrange for her surgery at St. Joseph Hospital. Through illness and accidents that cost the life of Josh's grandmother and seriously injured his mother, the family has been able to stay together. Dr. John Aur is proud that the staff at St. Jude has been able to help Josh and his family have a close family relationship. He does not feel that whatever was done was even unusual — it's all in a day's involvement for the St. Jude staff.

And Josh, at the age of three, understands and knows where his support comes from. During the Danny Thomas Memphis Golf Classic in 1980, some of the men from Albany took him to

the golf course. But all he really wanted to do was meet Danny Thomas "because you built my St. Jude Hospital."

Such continuous support is more difficult in larger communities, yet for more than twenty years, long-time ALSAC leaders like Sam Farhat in Lansing, Michigan; John Thomas in Wilkes-Barre, Pennsylvania; William Shaker in Terre Haute, Indiana; Al Harris in Kansas City, Missouri; Eddie Basha in Phoenix, Arizona; Jim Maloof in Peoria, Illinois, and other volunteers continue to mobilize their communities behind an annual campaign for St. Jude Children's Research Hospital.

Third party organizations are especially important to St. Jude Hospital and ALSAC. These organizations represent sororities, fraternities, civic and service groups, fraternal clubs, veterans groups and labor organizations. They include such diverse groups as Epsilon Sigma Alpha International, Tau Kappa Epsilon Fraternity, the Ice Skating Institute of America, the Fraternal Order of Eagles, the American Legion Auxiliary, the Ladies Auxiliary of the Veterans of Foreign

Joe Farris has brought gifts to the children at St. Jude Hospital since its beginning. Left, the early years, and, right, last year.

Wars, the Hotel and Restaurant Employees and Bartenders International Union. Also included are Alpha Delta Kappa, Beta Sigma Phi, Arthur Murray, Inc., Gamma Sigma Gamma, B'nai B'rith, Syrian Orthodox Youth Association, Motor Equipment Manufacturers Association, Optimist International, Jaycees and Jayceettes.

The Hotel and Restaurant Employees and Bartenders International Union has been involved with St. Jude since 1958. That year Danny Thomas received a call from Ed Miller, the union's general president, who told Danny that the union wanted to donate $50,000 to a non-

sectarian, non-racial charity. They had heard that he had one.

Danny told him the St. Jude story. Not long after his first discussion with Miller, Danny received a second call advising him that the union had raised its sights and would donate $250,000. When the money actually all came in it totalled more than $300,000.

After over twenty years of involvement, the union members still contribute more than a hundred thousand dollars a year through a self-imposed assessment of two cents a month per year, again emphasizing the importance of pennies!

The women of Epsilon Sigma Alpha International (ESA) have been involved with the hospital for over ten years. ESA International is the first non-collegiate sorority in America, founded in 1929. Today it is one of the world's most distinguished leadership-service organizations for women and its more than 33,000 members work together to aid those less fortunate than they and they work within their communities to help meet community needs.

In October of 1969, Jim Maloof, a dedicated supporter of St. Jude Hospital and member of the Board of Governors since the opening of the hospital, was given an opportunity to talk to the ESA Illinois chapter at a state meeting in Chicago. He told them the story of St. Jude Hospital, and at that meeting, the members voted to adopt St. Jude as their state project. At this meeting, visiting from Missouri, Iowa, Wisconsin and Indiana, were sisters active in their own home states.

They took the word back to their own chapters and in the spring of 1970 Jim Maloof was invited to attend and speak to the Iowa state convention. The members voted at that meeting to adopt St. Jude as their state project also.

The same thing happened in Missouri later that spring when Jim Maloof, with Mike Tamer in tow, attended their state convention. After hearing the story of St. Jude, the state of Wiscon-

Above: Danny Thomas receives the one million dollar check as promised from 1975 International President Jo Isquierdo. Far left: When Ed Miller, president of the Hotel and Restaurant Employees and Bartenders International Union announced in 1958 that the union had raised over $300,000 for Danny's hospital, Danny looked back over his shoulder at a statue of St. Jude "We're on our way!" Left: Accepting the check from Ed Miller.

sin quickly followed their sister states of Illinois, Iowa and Missouri.

Meanwhile, in October of 1969, Judy Lester and her husband, Morton, attended a Shower of Stars at the Diplomat Hotel in Hollywood, Florida. That evening she met Danny Thomas. She talked about ESA with him and he suggested that she talk with the national office in In-

dianapolis after she returned home. She did and became involved with various fund raising projects for St. Jude, especially the Teen Marches.

With Judy Lester and Jim Maloof both promoting St. Jude with Indiana ESA, the members voted in June of 1970 to work for St. Jude as one of its projects. But neither Judy nor Jim were content with state by state action — they wanted the national organization to adopt St. Jude as its national project.

The national convention was held in July of 1970 at St. Paul, Minnesota. Jim Maloof brought Danny Thomas, because Judy Lester had convinced ESA International that an Honorary Membership in ESA should be given to Danny at this meeting.

In 1971, Al Toler attended the meeting of the Southeastern Conference of ESA. Some of the individual chapters had been involved in raising funds for St. Jude but at this meeting the eleven states of the Southeastern Conference voted to adopt St. Jude as its regional project.

Also in 1971, Judy Lester met with the executive director of ESA — and they came up with the idea of a national project, a Million Dollar Cross Country Bike Ride, with each local chapter holding its own ride in addition to the national one. The International Council endorsed the idea naming it "ESA's Million Dollar Bike Ride."

Two years later Judy Lester was elected ESA International president and shortly after this St. Jude Hospital became the first International project of ESA. To date they have raised more than six million dollars for the hospital and the fourth floor of the new tower is named in their honor.

In 1975, three new "sisters" were voted into membership of ESA International — Danny Thomas, Jim Maloof and Al Toler! They attend as many national conventions as they possibly can and Jim Maloof has chalked up an impressive record of representing St. Jude before ESA groups in thirty-two states — at his own expense

Above: Danny Thomas and Judy Lester, 1973 ESA International president start off the Million Dollar Bike Ride alongside Royce and Billye Peterson, 1974-1975 cross-country riders. Right: ESA members visit the research floor dedicated to their organization.

and as a volunteer, of course, as are all St. Jude board of Governors members when they appear before any group to represent St. Jude Hospital.

In 1981, ESA International pledged to raise $800,000 to support research in neuroblastoma, the most common malignant solid tumor found in children. It was the first time that ESA had specifically addressed one area of the hospital's research in its efforts. Dr. Ann Hayes and Dr. Alexander Green met with representatives of ESA to discuss their research in neuroblastoma with them.

Another women's organization adopted St. Jude Hospital as its national project in 1980. Members of the United States Jayceettes had worked in local fund-raising since the beginning of the hospital but a decision was made to have a specific project within the hospital as a national effort.

Their goal is to fully fund the work of Dr. Gaston Rivera and Dr. Gary Dahl in their research in resitant lymphocytic leukemias.

Raising funds for St. Jude Hospital has become a project for some groups in foreign countries also. The International Elvis Presley Fan Club from Belgium visited St. Jude Hospital in 1980 while they were in Memphis for the anniversary of Elvis' death. They brought with them a check

St. Jude's Shower of Stars — Jerry Lewis

THIS FLOOR DEDICATED TO

ESA, INTERNATIONAL

FOR THEIR UNTIRING EFFORTS

ON BEHALF

OF

ST. JUDE CHILDREN'S RESEARCH

HOSPITAL

for $2,400 that they had raised from benefits held during the year in memory of Elvis. It was the second year that they had visited St. Jude and they promised to return each year with additional funds for the children being cared for in Elvis' home town.

Entertainers by the hundreds have supported Danny Thomas, fellow entertainer, in his dream. Many appeared with him while he was campaigning for the hospital with only a prayer and a picture. Jack Benny was one of these. Others, including Barbara Stanwyck, donated monies paid to them for guest appearances on television shows.

After the success of the two shows that were held in Memphis in 1955 and 1957, a series of Shower of Star shows were held in Memphis during the 1960's and into the 1970's. Names like Wayne Newton, Tennessee Ernie Ford, Sammy Davis, Jr., Paul Anka and Frank Sinatra all were regulars on these shows.

As a special bonus for the patients and staff at St. Jude Hospital the show business people also came to visit. In the early days the stars came to tour the hospital with Danny. In later years many who were in Memphis entertaining or who were just passing through the area stopped to visit with the children. Today, many still visit, some to renew old friendships and others to affirm their support of a fellow entertainer's dream.

Visitors are not confined to the entertainment field. Sports figures have also supported the hospital and many stars from golf to soccer have visited and entertained the patients, their families and staff.

Throughout the years entertainers and famous people have added their names to the personal appeals that went out through radio and television in ALSAC's appeal for funds.

In 1978 Celeste Hookings of Memphis decided it would be a great draw for St. Jude if Muhammed Ali were added to this list. He had visited the hospital in 1977 to talk with the children.

As Celeste tells anyone within the sound of her voice, it took a tragedy for her to devote her

---

Stars who appeared in St. Jude's Shower of Stars during the 1960's and into the 70's included Dinah Shore, Sammy Davis, Jr., Jerry Lewis, Totie Fields, Lynn Anderson, Tennessee Ernie Ford, Wayne Newton, Frank Sinatra and Bob Hope.

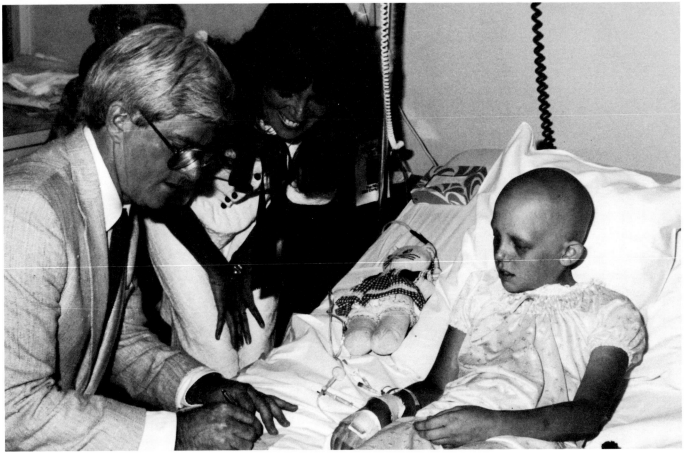

time to St. Jude and raising funds for it. Her son, John, a nationally ranked trampolinist, died in March of 1978 of leukemia at the age of 18.

Later that year she set out on her quest to elicit Ali's support. She visited his training camp in Deere Park, Pennsylvania. Ali was not there at the time but she made friends with the camp supervisor who introduced her to Ali when she returned. Ali assured Celeste that anything that was good for kids was worth his time. She offered him the microphone of her tape recorder and told him to start talking. There was no prepared script — he was to just say what he felt.

This is what the tape recorded:

"Hello, everybody, this is Muhammed Ali, the greatest fighter of all time. But the children at St. Jude Children's Research Hospital in Memphis, Tennessee, are in a fight greater than my fight with George Foreman, greater than my fight with Ken Norton and greater than my fight coming up in the Superdome with Leon Spinks."

"These children who are at St. Jude are special. The world doesn't know about their fight like

Through the years dignitaries, movie and television stars, musicians and athletes have visited St. Jude Hospital and its children. This page and the following show many of them who stop regularly to bring smiles to the faces of the patients.

they do about mine but they'll all be pulling for me and I'm pulling for these kids, and I want you to, too. Do everything you can. I'm dedicating this to the children at St. Jude Children's Research Hospital who are the greatest fighters of all times."

After the tape was completed, Ali was worried that it might not turn out to be usable. He insisted on recording a second message and told Celeste that if she found the tape was not good to let him know. She asked him if he would write on the outside of the cartridge that he gave her permission to use the tape.

Ali wrote, "I, Ali, O.K. you to use this tape." On the reverse side he added, "Service to others is the rent we pay for our room here on earth." Mike Tamer, "Mr. ALSAC," would have cheered him and his statement!

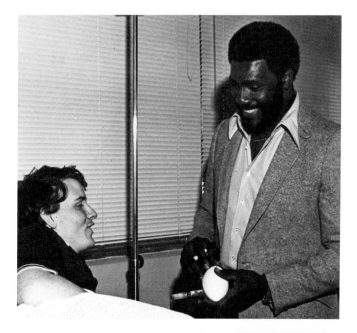

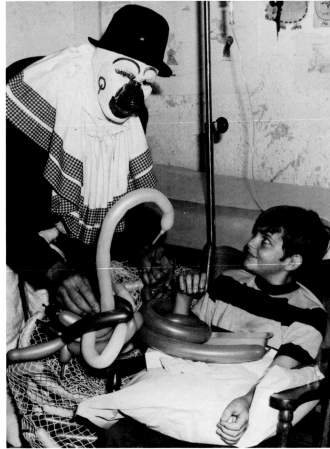

Prior to 1976 ALSAC's fund raising through the broadcast media had been largely confined to radio and radiothons.

The first of these were held in Detroit in 1968 through 1972. They were the brainchild of Jacquie Simo who conducted them. Jacquie had been interested in the hospital and in fund raising for it while working with her mother, Ethel Bekolay Horste, in the Detroit area on Teen Marches and the many other fund raising projects that kept Detroit leading the nation in fund-raising from 1964 through 1973 with no less than a quarter of a million dollars sent into national headquarters each year.

Jacquie had been nursed through two near-fatal illnesses but her family had never despaired and by the late 60's she was deeply involved in helping raise money for St. Jude Hospital. She designed the radiothon and successfully pro-

moted it in Detroit for four years. At the end of that period Mike Tamer hired her to work with the national office to direct the national radiothon program. She wrote the promotional materials and then went out into thirteen cities in one year to plan and hold radiothons.

During the 1970's radiothons were held across the country and were quite successful. The telethon format that was then being used by

---

Below: Singer Al Martino, Judy Norton from The Waltons, Eve Plumb from the Brady Bunch and Mrs. Rose Marie Thomas take calls during a Los Angeles Radiothon. Top right: Joe Shaker, ALSAC Board member helps feed the troops with hamburgers donated by McDonald's at a Chicago radiothon. Center right: Mark Blinoff, KMPC Program Director in Los Angeles gets some help on the telephones from Danny Thomas and Ed McMahon. Lower right: Richard Shadyac, Jack Alex and Marlo Thomas during a Washington radiothon.

other national organizations had been considered but had been rejected as being too expensive in relation to the amount of monies raised.

But in 1976, Jess Duboy, advertising man and ALSAC volunteer from Richmond, Virginia produced and directed a three-hour show using talented amateurs. This video tape was then blocked into short segments that allowed local live participation — with celebrities, check presentations and telephone activity — to work the entire package into a five hour telethon. This format was well received in other cities but it did demonstrate the need for nationally known celebrity participation.

Danny Thomas reluctantly agreed to host a live telethon in 1977. With Kate Jackson as his co-host he presented a five-hour show in Los Angeles that raised a staggering $338,664! When the results were in, Danny was estatic. "I can't remember why I never wanted to do this," he exclaimed.

Dena Howell, first admitted to St. Jude as a patient with acute lymphocytic leukemia in 1977, and her two healthy children join Jim Maloof at the 1980 Telethon in Peoria, Illinois.

Kate Jackson and Danny Thomas chat with Ricardo Montalban during the first live Telethon in Los Angeles in 1977.

Even better results were achieved when the show tapes were edited down to a two and a half hour show and used for more than twenty mini-telethons across the country.

In 1978, Danny added a live New York City Memorial Day special to the Los Angeles production, bringing top Broadway stars to the support of St. Jude. The release of St. Jude's award-winning film "A Child of Us All," came in time to add a strong message to the new videotaped show.

In 1979 Memphis was added to Danny's schedule of live shows and again the results were spectacular.

The next year brought a special taping before a live audience at the Frontier Hotel in Las Vegas with such stars as Joan Rivers, Wayne Newton, Milton Berle, Tony Bennett, Norm Crosby and others lending their talents. This was then used for the traveling show.

By 1980 the success of the telethons had over-taxed the abilities of the regional office staffs to organize and service them. Again, a new concept became available as the old one appeared to be peaking. The summer of 1981 brought film crews from the Russ Reid Company in Los Angeles to St. Jude Hospital and into some pa-tient homes to film a new, scripted television show. Live local segments and pure entertainment segments were discarded in favor of a special featuring the hospital staff, patients and selected entertainers. The approval of the Board of this concept meant that the ALSAC staff would no longer need to spend innumerable hours producing television shows, and ALSAC could anticipate millions of dollars in increased broadcast revenues for the hospital.

The special is programmed to go into more than a hundred cities across the United States and into Hawaii, before the end of 1982, reaching far more persons than ever have been reached with the St. Jude story.

With the tremendous increase in its broadcast fund-raising programs, ALSAC created a Department of Broadcasting in 1981 to supervise the steady growth that began with a radiothon in Detroit in 1968.

The Memphis telethon is held each year at the same time the Danny Thomas Memphis Golf Classic is played. In 1960 a check from the then-named Memphis Open was presented to St. Jude Hospital for $600.00. That began a continuing involvement for the tournament and the hospital. Some years later it was re-named the Danny Thomas Memphis Classic and would attract "names" from both the professional and amateur world of golf.

Since leaving the White House, former president Gerald Ford has played in the classic's Pro-Am tournament. The year he left the White House, 1977, he shot a hole-in-one at the tourna-

Above: Members of the Memphis Firefighters Association, who have supported St. Jude since its beginning, join Danny at the Memphis Telethon. Below: In 1960, before St. Jude Hospital opened its doors, Joe Connors and Curtis Person, Sr. presented Danny Thomas with a check for $600.00 from the Memphis Open.

"THE SHOT HEARD 'ROUND THE WORLD"
PRESIDENT
GERALD R. FORD
HOLE-IN-ONE

Danny motivates ALSAC staff

ment. He gave the ball to the hospital to be auctioned to the highest bidder. The high bid was made by Joe Haggar of Dallas, Texas, a long-time supporter of the hospital. He gave St. Jude a check for the ball and then presented it back to Gerald Ford for his trophy case.

In 1981 Bob Hope and Phil Donahue joined the Pro-Am line-up for the kids at the hospital. The tournament now raises hundreds of thousands of dollars each year for the hospital.

The patients and the staff are especially delighted when Lee Trevino wins. When he won his third championship in 1980, he made good on a promise he had made after winning his first championship in 1971. He returned $5,000 of his winnings to St. Jude, bringing his total contributions from winnings at the Danny Thomas Memphis Classic to $21,500.

In 1980 he remarked, "I guess the only reason I won was because all those kids over at St. Jude were praying for me because they knew I always give them that $5,000!"

With the expansion of all these programs and consolidation of control in the Memphis office, it was apparent that ALSAC needed computer

Opposite page upper left: Lee Trevino gets a winner's check and gives part of it back to Danny for his hospital. Upper right: Jerry Pate prepares to make his now famous dive into the water at the 18th hole after winning the 1981 Danny Thomas Memphis Classic. Left: Danny Thomas unveils a plaque commemorating the hole-in-one made by President Gerald Ford in 1977.

assistance in both its fund-raising and accounting operations. In 1975, donor records were still being kept on a manual system, with the exception of those responding to the national direct mail campaign. Under the direction of Dennis Morlok, Director of Finance and Administrative Services, ALSAC moved into computerization and improved management systems. It started with time sharing with the hospital business office computer, but promptly outgrew this arrangement.

By 1979, processing of gifts, broadcast pledges, thank you letters, and CDP requirements made it necessary to retain a computer firm in Nashville to shift some of the work load and accomplish the anticipated move of the direct mail donor file to Memphis. This provided time to plan for the future, and in January 1982, a Data Processing Department was created, charged with bringing ALSAC completely into the computer age. By mid 1983, ALSAC will have its own computers, installed in 1982, completely on line, for management and fund raising, including the control of mailing the massive quantities of mail to prospective donors.

Perhaps the most striking aspect of the spectacular growth of ALSAC is that its 125 full-time employees in 1982 still make it one of the smallest of all national charity staffs. Even with a dramatic increase in programs and income, ALSAC remains very dependent on its loyal and dedicated volunteers across the country to continue to fund the miraculous accomplishments of St. Jude Children's Research Hospital.

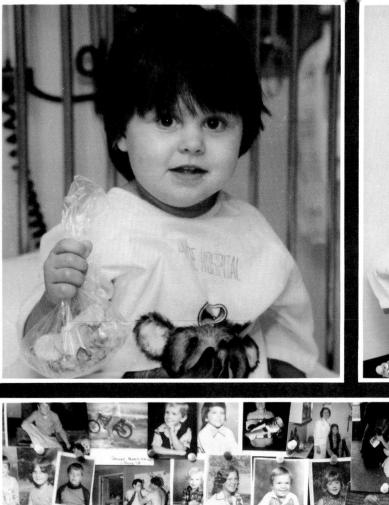

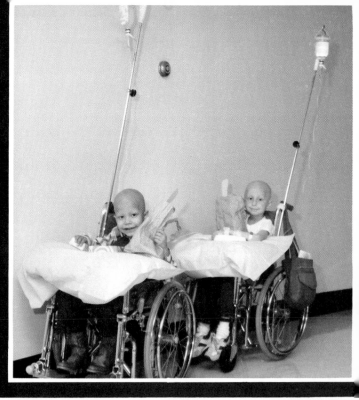

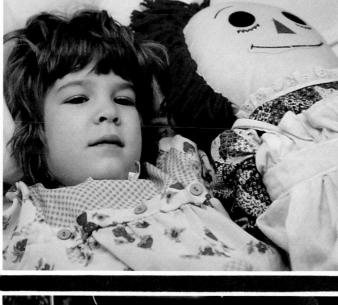

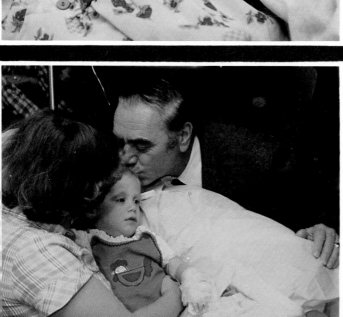

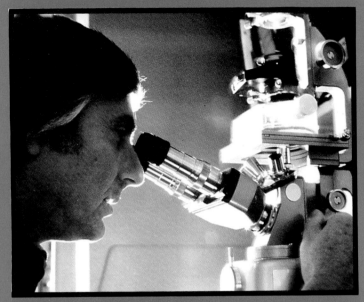

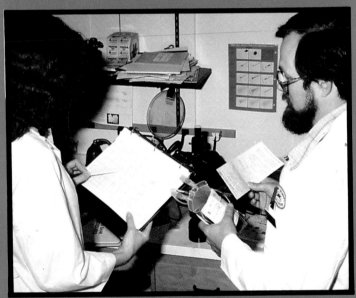
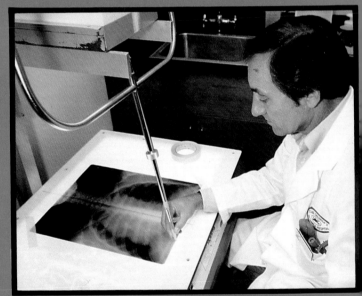

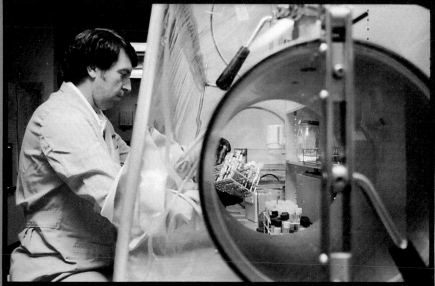

"It is a job that requires seven days a week, thirty days a month and three hundred sixty-five days a year. The worst thing is going through life without leaving a mark of your passage. I think we have left our tracks. I think we are doing our job."

"Thank you, God, for my remission today and for giving me one more tomorrow."

Reaching For The Stars
The Next Twenty Years . . . and Beyond

Twenty years after St. Jude Children's Research Hospital opened its doors it has achieved heights never believed possible by those involved with it since the beginning. The small research center that Danny Thomas had dreamed of has become the number one center in the world for research and treatment of catastrophic diseases in children.

Under treatment are more than four thousand patients with more added to the roster each day. The cost of operating the hospital has reached almost a hundred thousand dollars a day! Of this, forty percent is used for medical services, thirty percent for laboratory research, twenty percent for clinical research and the remaining ten percent for education and training in research services.

Treatment procedures developed at St. Jude appear in every relevant medical textbook and journal and the hospital is recognized as a world authority in the development of such treatment.

And, St. Jude Hospital has added much to the reputation of the city of Memphis as being truly the "City of Good Abode." Ed Barry, Chairman of the Board of Governors, says of the hospital and its relation to the city, "I don't know of anything happening in the city that has brought more honorable praise and recognition than St. Jude Children's Research Hospital."

"Today, no matter where you go, this country or other countries, people know about it. I was going through a factory in Dublin, Ireland, recently where they do the Irish Sweepstakes tickets. When the people were told that I was from Memphis they knew all about St. Jude Hospital in Memphis, Tennessee."

Another Memphian, Sam Cooper, retired president of Humko Products, also feels that St. Jude Hospital has made a great impact

Another Memphian, Sam Cooper, retired president of Humko Products, also feels that St. Jude Hospital has made a great impact on the community of Memphis itself. For years the focus of interest in the city was on cotton and lumber. Now, one of the major features of Memphis is its Medical Center, and St. Jude Hospital has played an important part in bringing it to its position of importance.

He also credits the Memphis community for its support of the hospital. Several years ago when he was the recipient of an award given by the National Conference of Christians and Jews, and Danny Thomas was the guest speaker at the dinner, the two men became acquainted.

Very shortly after that meeting Mr. Copper lost a daughter to cancer, bringing the harsh reality of the disease into his home. Some months later a group of doctors from the University of Tennessee asked him if he would help them raise two million dollars for their cancer research. He recalls that he agreed to help because, "One of four families in this country is touched by cancer. If you are not, you ought to get down on your knees every night and thank the man upstairs for being so blessed. If you have gone through this ordeal you have to be as dedicated as you can to prevent someone else from suffering as you did."

Two or three weeks after meeting with this group, Mr. Cooper received a call from Danny Thomas asking him if he would help St. Jude Hospital raise two million dollars to pay off the cost of the new addition.

Cooper told Danny that he had just made a commitment to help the University of Tennessee raise two million dollars and he didn't know if Memphis would go for two drives of two million dollars each for the same cause, cancer research.

When he talked it over that evening with his wife, she asked him a direct question, "Do you think you could raise four million in one drive?" After thinking it over, he called the chancellor at the university and said he was not backing away from his promise, but how would the chancellor feel about joining forces with St. Jude Hospital and splitting whatever was raised between the two institutions. He agreed and a four million dollar drive was launched.

The committee started from scratch and the people of Memphis and the surrounding area really "stood tall." Ninety days from the "scratch" start, over 4.3 million dollars had been raised. And, Sam Cooper recalls that he got a big salary to head up the drive ... it only cost him $50,000!

But his satisfaction really came from a meeting with the transportation committee of the drive. A man who worked for a trucking company came up to him and said that he wanted to thank him for what he was doing. The man was the father of an eight year old son who had leukemia. He told how the doctors had given up and told him the only thing he could do was to take the child to St. Jude Hospital. The youngster responded to their treatment and was doing well.

"That was my pay-off," said Sam Cooper.

There have been remarkable improvements in the knowledge of how to treat children with cancer and in the results of those treatments. The most important facet was learning that cancer in children is not necessarily a fatal disease.

Now the emphasis at St. Jude is on life and living instead of death and dying. The researchers and clinicians are looking for more effective methods of treatment and for additional research to provide a better understanding of all childhood cancers.

The goal of both the clinicians and the basic scientists is not just a cure but a prevention, as well. It is not the nature of the staff at St. Jude to be satisfied with past achievements. Each step ahead only pushes the staff harder toward the completion of the next step.

Those who have been, and are now, deeply involved with St. Jude Hospital are looking toward a cure. Dr. Pinkel, the first medical director, believes that the surest cure will come from the laboratories of the basic scientists. Until that happens — and until a cause is known — clinical researchers will continue to refine methods of treating the disease by the total therapy program, first developed at St. Jude, and now in use around the world.

Dr. Simone, associate director for clinical research, when asked about a cure, answers, "I think that is sometime off, but I think it is possible. That's what we're working toward." Dr. Simone also feels that the solution will come

---

"It is a job that requires seven days a week, thirty days a month and 365 days a year. To me the worst thing is going through life without leaving a mark of your passage. I think we have left our tracks. I think we are doing our job."

from the laboratories of the basic scientists. No one knows what direction help is coming from, but he expects no miracles.

"We don't have any gangbuster programs. The history of cancer treatment is inch by inch — there's no great breakthrough. Everything has been very slow and we don't expect any sudden dramatic disclosures."

Simone also observes, "The hardest thing to come up with are new ideas. Research generates new ideas. You need a critical mass of people who are dedicated to developing those ideas and trying them out and taking them and applying them to future patients. Our staff is the most important element, and we are going to generate new approaches and new treatments that will be better than in the past."

Dr. Mauer is also looking forward to another building since the existing structures are rapidly being filled to overflowing. As the number of patients grows in the clinical studies area it will eventually be necessary to take over the space in the original building that is now being used for basic research. He visualizes the next major structure as another research tower, possibly with some parking space (badly needed), that would be constructed behind the existing seven-story tower.

But, until that happens another staged development of remodeling and reconstruction is underway. Dr. Len Johnson joined the staff in July of 1981 and is in charge of bone marrow transplant, a new program. Prior to this time any patient needing a bone marrow transplant had to be sent to another facility across the country.

To accommodate this new program the radiotherapy department was expanded to include three new pieces of equipment necessary for the bone marrow program. This was accomplished by the expansion of the current radiotherapy department into a parking area directly behind the existing unit. This is the only actual construction phase — all other changes will involve remodeling existing areas. This addition was completed in the fall of 1982.

At the same time the basement area that was vacated when the animal facility moved into its new building is to be remodeled to allow addi-

---

"There's a lot to be done but we've made the big jump. Just like the triple jump in the Olympics — the first jump is always longer, the second is less long and the third even less."

tional space for virology laboratories, biochemistry laboratories and nutrition. Housekeeping and Central Sterile Supply is to be consolidated and enlarged.

After the wing that now houses virology has been vacated it will be remodeled for clinical laboratory expansion. Completion of this is planned in the spring of 1983.

Along with the addition to the radiotherapy department extensive changes will be made in that wing to include the addition of a Tomography unit to Diagnostic Imaging, enlarging the facilities of the psychology department, relocating the patient photography and respiration therapy from the basement to the first floor, moving nutrition from its borrowed space in the tower to the first floor along with pharmacokinetics which has also been occupying borrowed space in the tower. These stages are to be completed by July of 1984.

Every effort is being made to effectively design all space for its most effective and optimum use. And that will be very necessary since Dr. Mauer is talking about expanding the areas of basic research. One area under consideration might develop if the clinical areas should develop a program for taking care of children with brain tumors. Basic research would then be needed that would help the clinicians understand the brain and the responses of the nervous tissues of the brain — studies where abnormal tissue could be contrasted with the normal function of the brain.

Neurobiology would be another area of basic research to help develop a program to care for children with brain tumors.

Again, Dr. Mauer reflects that the doctors at St. Jude are recognizing that there may be some kinds of cancers with a built-in predisposition, that someone born with the increased sensitivity to whatever it is that triggers the formation of the cancer. An area of research might be a basic science group working on genetics to help understand how something can be inherited and passed on to future generations. In this area, data studies now being conducted by the Bio-statistics division will be invaluable.

The one thing that will happen, most certainly, is that St. Jude Hospital's dedicated staff will use everything at their command to research and find the cause and cure of the catastrophic diseases that are still killing children.

"It was a utopian medical complex . . . the ideal of some of the dreamers. There was hardly any other place in the world where a hospital took on complete medical care. It was a dream . . . almost beyond belief."

ALSAC Looks to the Future

While the needs of the hospital are increasing each year and, as more dollars are needed to maintain it, the burden falls on the broad shoulders of the ALSAC organization. When Danny Thomas asked his people to help him in the maintenance of St. Jude Hospital he felt that $300,000 a year would do it. The 1984 or 1985 budget could reach at least 50 million dollars for just one year!

Bud Rashid, executive director of ALSAC, sees it as a staggering task. "The more successful we are, the larger the burden becomes. The more children who are living, the more costly it is going to be for us to keep the institution going because each patient is a patient for life. The patient load increases year after year."

But Bud Rashid and the ALSAC staff are delighted that the challenge does exist ... they are pleased that more and more children are living and fewer are being lost to their illnesses. They are more than willing to assume the additional expense from year to year.

The costs facing ALSAC in the 1980's are staggering. In 1980 the cost of one day's hospitalization for a child, including all hospital services, was $612.00. One outpatient visit, including all services, was $136.00. One day of chemotheraphy administered intravenously to leukemia or solid tumor patients was $415.00. The cost of a surgical suite, including anesthesia, for a major operation was $1,400.00. An artificial leg (above the knee), quadrilateral, total contact with pneumatic knee was $1,500.00 and with growing children, several of these are needed before a child reaches full growth.

Rashid feels that the competition for charity dollars is also becoming more intense each year, that people are concentrating their charity dollars in a limited number of charities. That is the reason he feels the backbone of any organization is its volunteer strength throughout the country. A charity cannot really be effective without a broad base of volunteers to collect the donations and conduct the fund-raising events.

In the future, he would like to see an endowment large enough to be a self-sustaining trust for the hospital. There are some problems with creating an endowment of this type since the public is reluctant to give dollars to an endowment — they want to know that the dollars they are giving now are being used now. This is one of the many problems that Rashid and the Board are studying, trying to find ways to increase the revenues without a greatly increased burden on the average person who contributes so willingly to the hospital.

But while this is under study, the people across the nation who have supported Danny Thomas' dream since 1945 are still working, still giving, still meeting the increased dollar obligations of St. Jude Children's Research Hospital. They have not wavered or faltered in their support.

Bud Rashid sums it all up when he says, "We have come a long way from our earliest beginnings. I only hope that all our successes will not lull us into a feeling of complacency. There are so many more avenues of research available to us; there are so many more children who have not yet responded to our treatment procedures; there are so many more childhood diseases requiring expanded research effort. We still have further heights to climb and only our volunteers can insure the future."

"The only thanks I want is that every day I want to hear about some kid who is still living because there is a St. Jude Hospital . . ."

And the Man who Started It All . . .

"I get tired sometimes and every time I think I'm going to quit I visit St. Jude . . . and going through the hospital and seeing those kids . . . especially the ones who aren't going to make it . . . I just go out and re-dedicate myself. I really just want to go out into the street and mug somebody for his money if he won't give it to me." This is what Danny Thomas says today.

He recalls that, "Mike (Tamer) was strong like that. Mike didn't believe in begging. I learned that from Mike. He didn't beg our people . . . he demanded of them, that they come along and do this thing. Today I demand a dollar from people because that dollar can save a life. The only right I have for such a demand is the work that is being done. We're proving it . . ."

"We see the kids that survived from 1962 to 1967 and they are not kids any more. They're adults and living a good life, some with children of their own. If we'd done nothing more than that it would have been worth it."

Danny Thomas also talks about an endowment. He believes that a three hundred million dollar endowment plus the government grants to the hospital would take care of the needs and growth for the future. In the meantime he says, "I drop a hint here and there that we're looking for a lot of money. Also we're looking for a lot of little money."

"I'd rather have a million people give me a dollar than one give me a million. Then you've got a million people involved. I was lying awake one night and thinking about how we could keep the hospital going and I remembered the old phrase, 'I wouldn't give two cents for their chances'. I laid there and figured that if fifty million people would give just two cents a week for five years the work at St. Jude would be funded in perpetuity . . . and thousands and thousands of children's lives could be saved."

To Danny Thomas, everytime he sees a child hurting reaffirms his vow and his goal. That children should die before their time is totally unacceptable to him.

"It really is miraculous how it all came about, but St. Jude works in strange ways." Danny says "It's a miracle" often. He believes in miracles. And he has taught others to believe. He has lifted his patron saint, St. Jude Thaddeus, the patron saint of the impossible, hopeless and difficult cases, from relatively obscurity in those late years of the 1930's to a position of high esteem among people all over the world.

Together, with the help of millions of their friends, Danny Thomas and St. Jude have proved that there are no longer totally "impossible" cases of catastrophic diseases in the lives of the kids he loves.

It is not too much to ask that in the future his hospital, like that other entertainer so many years ago and his hospital, will become completely endowed. And that his hospital would some day have no patient that would die because there was no cure for the child's disease.

Dr. Alvin Mauer and Danny Thomas — honored jointly by the St. Boniface General Hospital Research Foundation for their efforts in the fight against catastrophic childhood diseases. Given annually in recognition of support to or participation in outstanding medical research, the award cites Dr. Mauer, Mr. Thomas, the patrons, the staff and the patients of St. Jude Hospital, "who have created an institution which serves as a living testament to the ability of the human spirit to conquer adversity and as a shining example of the fusion of science and humanity."

ROLL OF HONORS — 1957 TO PRESENT
BOARD OF GOVERNORS AND BOARD OF DIRECTORS

The Board of Directors of ALSAC and the Board of Governors of St. Jude Children's Hospital consist of volunteer members who serve without compensation to provide the oversight and general guidance to the professional staffs of the two organizations. Since records from the earliest years are incomplete, this listing has been reconstructed from the best data available, applying current terminology and cross-checking against unofficial sources. Any omission or error is purely unintentional.

Senator James Abourezk	1973-1976
Alex Aboussie First Vice President, Board of Directors 1962-1963	1961-1968
Edward Aboussie	1967-1969
Louis Aboussie	1962-1965
Anthony Abraham First Vice President, Board of Directors 1960-1961	1958-Present
Moris Adland, M.D.	1973-1978
Alice Albert	1980-Present
Sister Alfreda, O.S.F.	1960-1962
Robert S. Andrews	1974-1975
George D. Attea	1962-1969, 1973-1975
Mitchell Awn	1966-1969
Joseph A. Ayoub	1957-1974
Joseph A. Ayoub	1957-Present
Edward F. Barry Chairman, Board of Governors, 1960-1982 Chairman Emeritus, 1982-	1960-Present
Naef K. Basile, M.D. Second Vice-President, Board of Directors 1957-1959	1957-1978
Sister M. Bernardine, O.S.F.	1963-1968
Michael Berry	1974-1979
Elizabeth Beshara	1968-1980
James Michael Beshara	1981-Present
William F. Bitar	1959-1963
William Boonisar	1970-1977
Michael Borane	1962-1963

John Bourisk, Sr.	1960-Present
Thomas Boutrous, M.D.	1957-1967
Nat Buring	1963-1976
V. Reo Campian	1967-Present
John Ford Canale Secretary, Board of Governors 1962-1982	1960-1982
Elias J. Chalhub	1957-1975
Anthony Colonna	1978-Present
Sam Cooper Second Vice Chairman, Board of Governors, 1979 First Vice-President, Board of Directors, 1978 Second Vice-President, Board of Directors, 1976-1977	1974-1979
George Coury	1975-1979
George P. Dakmak Second Vice President, Board of Directors, 1964-1965	1958-1965
Edward Mike Davis	1970
S. Robert Davis	1971-1973
Peter C. Decker First Vice-President, Board of Directors, 1982- Second Vice President, Board of Directors, 1980-1981	1971-1976, 1978-Present
Richard J. Deeb Second Vice-President, Board of Directors, 1960-1962	1958-1963
Roy J. Deeb	1962-1963
Joseph Demos	1967-1970
L. W. Diggs, M.D.	1960-1975
Patrick Doyle	1978-Present
John T. Dwyer	1960-1965

B. D. Eddie First Vice-President, Board of Directors, 1957-1960	1957-1969	William Harrington, M.D.	1975-1978
		Albert F. Harris	1968-Present
Elias N. Ede	1982-Present	William Hassan, Jr., Ph.D.	1975-1982
William Edwards	1957-1960	Theodore Hazer	1977-Present
Dr. Edward M. Eissey	1978-Present	Ethel Bekolay Horste Second Vice-President, Board of Directors, 1982-	1957-Present
Eddie Elias	1967-1972		
George Elias, Jr. Executive Vice-President, Board of Directors, 1982-1983 First Vice-President, Board of Directors, 1980-1981 Second Vice-President, Board of Directors, 1979	1972-Present	Albert Jamail Treasurer, Board of Directors, 1973-	1970-Present
		Albert Joseph Vice-Chairman, Board of Governors, 1982- Executive Vice-President, Board of Directors, 1978-1979 First Vice-President, Board of Directors, 1976-1977	1957-Present
William F. Farha	1957-1965		
Sam Farhat Second Vice-President, Board of Directors, 1972-1973	1970-Present	George Joseph	1961-1962
		Joseph A. Kawie	1965-1975
Maury Foladare	1960-Present	Joseph Karam	1968-1974
Mrs. Mitchell Forzley	1957-1963	James A. Kinney	1982-Present
Fred P. Gattas, Sr. Chairman, Board of Governors, 1982- Vice Chairman, Board of Governors, 1962-1982 Secretary, Board of Governors, 1960-1962	1957-Present	Abe Lastfogel	1960-Present
		Judy Lester	1976-Present
		Daniel Levinthal, M.D.	1960-1978
Joseph P. Gattas, Jr.	1962-1976	Gilbert Levy, M.D.	1960-1975
Ben Geller	1965-1978	Albert Lian	1980-Present
Minor George	1957-1969	James Lofland	1961-1962
Paul George	1968-Present	George Maloof Second Vice President, Board of Directors, 1962-1963	1958-Present
Halim G. Habib, M.D.	1964-Present		
James S. Haboush Treasurer, Board of Directors, 1957-1962	1957-1962	James Maloof Executive Vice President, Board of Directors, 1972-1973 First Vice President, Board of Directors, 1970-1971 Second Vice President, Board of Directors, 1968-1969	1958-Present
Bill Haddad	1973-1978		
Wade Haddad	1973-Present		
Joseph Haggar, Jr.	1962-1968	Al Mansour	1975-1978
Emile Hajar Executive Vice-President, Board of Directors, 1970-1971 First Vice-President, Board of Directors, 1968-1969 Second Vice-President, Board of Directors, 1966-1967	1962-Present	Frederick M. Marshall	1963
		Albert Maykel Executive Vice-President, Board of Directors, 1960-1961 Second Vice-President, Board of Directors, 1959	1957-1980

Mike McKool	1963
Howard Metzembaum	1974-1976
Tony Michaels	1970-1975
Fred Mickel	1963-1978
Ed S. Miller	1971-1976
Richard Naify	1974-1980
Victor Najjar, M.D.	1968-Present
George Najour	1968-1969
Floyd Nassif, M.D.	1964-1975
Edward J. Peters	1968-1971
Baddia J. Rashid Executive Vice-President, Board of Directors, 1962-1963 First Vice President, Board of Directors, 1974-1975 Second Vice-President, Board of Directors, 1960-1961	1959-1976
Joseph G. Rashid Executive Vice-President, Board of Directors, 1957-1959	1957-1968
LaVonne Rashid	1957-1974
Edward W. Reed, M.D.	1978-Present
Emile Reggie First Vice-President, Board of Directors, 1972-1973 Second Vice-President, Board of Directors, 1970-1971	1957-1977, 1981-Present
George Risk	1962-1975
Sister M. Rita, O.S.F.	1966-1973
Joseph Robbie Executive Vice-President, Board of Directors, 1966-1967 First Vice-President, Board of Directors, 1964-1965	1961-1979
J. Richard Rossie	1980-1982
Louis Saad, Sr.	1966-1977
George Sabbag Executive Vice-President, Board of Directors, 1976-1977 Second Vice-President, Board of Directors, 1974-1975	1972-Present

John Sakakini	1957-1960
Robert T. Salem	1968-1973
Sam Salem First Vice President, Board of Directors, 1960-1961	1957-1961
Walter Schlesinger, M.D.	1968-1970
W. W. Scott Treasurer, Board of Governors, 1960-1962	1960-1962
Richard C. Shadyac Executive Vice-President, Board of Directors, 1964-1965, 1974-1975 Secretary, Board of Governors, 1982-	1963-Present
Joseph Shaker	1975-Present
George Simon Executive Vice-President, Board of Directors, 1980-1981 First Vice-President, Board of Directors, 1979 Second Vice-President, Board of Directors, 1978	1962-Present
George R. Simon Treasurer, Board of Directors, 1962-1972	1960-1978
George Sissler	1960
Edward D. Soma, M.D. Executive Vice-President, Board of Directors, 1968-1969 First Vice-President, Board of Directors, 1966-1967	1966-Present
Sister Mary Stephanina, O.S.F.	1960-1972
Morris Stoller	1960-Present
Victor Swyden Executive Vice-President, Board of Directors, 1960-1961	1958-1961
Michael F. Tamer	1957-1974
Adeeb Thomas, D.M.D., M.S.	1966-1982
Danny Thomas President, Board of Directors, 1957-Present	1957-Present
John J. Thomas	1969-Present
Marlo Thomas	1972-1975
R. David Thomas	1978-1981
Terre Thomas	1980-Present
Thomas C. Thomas	1962-1965

Esther Uhelski	1973-1975	

Bernie Wagner	1969-1973
Rich White	1975-1978
Robert Woolf	1975-1978
Monsour C. Zanaty	1959-1961
Paul Ziffren	1960

BOARD OF DIRECTORS AND GOVERNORS

1982

The same volunteers serve without compensation as the ALSAC Board of Directors and the Board of Governors of St. Jude Children's Research Hospital.

OFFICERS

ALSAC

Danny Thomas
President

George Simon
Executive Vice-President

George Elias, Jr.
First Vice-President

Peter Decker, Jr.
Second Vice-President

Albert Jamail
Treasurer

SJCRH

Edward F. Barry
Chairman

Fred P. Gattas, Sr.
Vice-Chairman

John Ford Canale†
Secretary
(deceased Aug. 4, 1982)

BOARD MEMBERS

**Mr. Anthony Abraham
Miami, FL

Mrs. Alice Rose Albert
San Francisco, CA

Mr. Joseph A. Ayoub
Boston, MA

---

*Mr. Edward F. Barry
Memphis, TN

Mr. James M. Beshara
Youngstown, OH

Mr. John J. Bourisk, Sr.
Lewiston, ME

Mr. V. Reo Campian
Bloomfield Hills, MI

*†Mr. John Ford Canale
Memphis, TN

Mr. Anthony Colonna
Wilkes-Barre, PA

*Mr. Peter G. Decker, Jr.
Norfolk, VA

*Mr. Patrick J. Doyle, Sr.
Palos Park, IL

Dr. Edward M. Eissey
Lake Worth, FL

*Mr. George Elias, Jr.
Miami, FL

Mr. Sam G. Farhat
Lansing, MI

*Mr. Fred P. Gattas, Sr.
Memphis, TN

Mr. Paul George
Liverpool, NY

Mrs. Terre Thomas Gordon
Beverly Hills, CA

Halim G. Habib, M.D.
Roslindale, MA

Mr. Wade Haddad
Cuyahoga Falls, OH

*Mr. Emile H. Hajar
West Roxbury, MA

---

*Mr. Albert F. Harris
Kansas City, MO

*William E. Hassan, Jr., Ph.D
Boston, MA

Mr. Theodore Hazer
Omaha, NE

**Mrs. Ethel Horste
Detroit, MI

*Mr. Albert Jamail
Houston, TX

*Mr. Albert Joseph
Des Plaines, IL

Mr. Abe Lastfogel
Beverly Hills, CA

**Mrs. Judy Lester
Seymour, IN

Mr. Albert William Lian
New York, NY

Mr. George Maloof
Cleveland, OH

**Mr. James A. Maloof
Peoria, IL

Victor A. Najjar, M.D.
Boston, MA

Edward W. Reed, M.D.
Memphis, TN

Mr. Emile Reggie
Crowley, LA

Mr. J. Richard Rossie
Memphis, TN

*Mr. George Sabbag
Westwood, MA

*Mr. Richard C. Shadyac
Annandale, VA

KEY PERSONNEL
St. Jude Children's Research Hospital

FACULTY

Dr. Alvin Mauer
Director

Dr. Allan Granoff
Associate Director of Basic
Research

Dr. Joseph V. Simone
Associate Director of Clinical
Research

Mr. R. L. Harrington
Associate Director of
Administration

Dr. Frank Adler
Chairman of Immunology

Mr. Larry Barker
Director, Clinical Pharmacy

Dr. Costan Berard
Chairman of Pathology

Dr. Raymond Blakley
Chairman of Pharmacology

Dr. Lawrence T. Ch'ien
Chief, Neurology-Psychology

Dr. Thomas Coburn
Chief of Diagnostic Imaging

Dr. Gary Dahl
Co-Director of the Leukemia
Service

Dr. William E. Evans
Director, Pharmacokinetics
Division

Dr. Sandor Feldman
Chief, Pediatrics

Dr. Stephen George
Director of Biostatistics

Dr. Alexander Green
Director of the Solid Tumor
Service

Dr. F. Ann Hayes
Hematology-Oncology (Solid
Tumor Service)

Dr. Walter Hughes
Chairman of Infectious
Diseases

Dr. H. Omar Hustu
Chief of Radiotherapy

Dr. F. Leonard Johnson
Chief, Bone Marrow
Transplantation Service

Dr. George Marten
Chief, Psychiatry

Dr. Martin Morrison
Chairman of Biochemistry

Dr. Sharon Murphy
Co-Director of the Leukemia
Service

Dr. Charles B. Pratt
Clinical Therapeutics

Dr. Elizabeth I. Thompson
Coordinator, Clinical Training
Program

Dr. Paul Zee
Chief, Nutrition and
Metabolism

ADMINISTRATIVE

Mr. Richard Asbury
Assistant Director for
Administration

211

1982 NATIONAL ADVISORY COUNCIL

Published by:

ALSAC
POST OFFICE BOX 3704
MEMPHIS, TN 38103

CREDITS

All photographs are by the Audio-Visual Communications department of St. Jude Children's Research Hospital, Jerry Luther, director, and the following:

The Commercial Appeal, Memphis, Tennessee.

The Press Scimitar, Memphis, Tennessee.

Frank Alexander, Alexander and Associates, Washington, D.C.

B & L Photographers, Indianapolis, Indiana.

Chase, Ltd., Washington, D.C.

The Chicago Catholic

Flaherty's Studio, Buffalo, New York.

Maurice C. Hartwick, Detroit, Michigan.

Hastings-Willinger & Associates, Cleveland, Ohio.

E. H. Jaffe, Memphis, Tennessee.

Los Angeles Times, Los Angeles, California.

Salem Nassiff, Manchester, Connecticut.

B. W. Neuffer, Detroit, Michigan.

Lee Shively, Shreveport Times, Shreveport, Louisiana.

Star News, Hollywood, California.

Barney A. Sterling, Chicago, Illinois.

Westrich Photograph, St. Louis, Missouri.